A
GUIDE
TO
HISTORIC HOUSES
IN OHIO
OPEN TO THE PUBLIC
SECOND EDITION

Published by
The National Society of the Colonial Dames of America in
the State of Ohio

Compiled by
Elizabeth P. Allyn - Chairperson Historical Activities 1984
Elisabeth H. Tuttle - Vice Chairperson Historical Activities 1984

Second Edition Revised by
Katharine F. Willi - Chairperson Historical Activities 1996

Dedicated to Elizabeth P. Allyn without whose imagination and diligence this book could not have been published.

Library of Congress Catalog Card Number 84-062235

Second Edition, 1996
Printed in the U.S. A. by
Odyssey Press Inc.
373 Enterprise Drive
Westerville, Ohio 43081

ISBN: 0-9650831-0-1

Cover
C.C. Thompson Home

CONTENTS

PAGE

INTRODUCTION

This guide, published by The National Society of the Colonial Dames of America in the State of Ohio, is a multipurpose work. It may be used as a tour guide, a guide to Ohio residential architecture, or as a reference to Ohio's rich and varied history. Geographic location, architectural and historical information, furnishings, collections and visiting hours are included for each house. Immediately following the name of the house is the date it was built. Other dates denote additions or architectural changes. The owner and/or administrators of the buildings are noted. The cutoff date for listing in this guide is the 1930's.

The National Register of Historic Places is the nation's official list of properties which are significant in American history, architecture, archaeology, engineering, and culture. The National Register is maintained by the U.S. Department of the Interior, and includes properties of local, state, and national importance. Ohio has more than 3000 historic sites which have been placed on the National Register. Houses that are listed on the National Register of Historic Places are specified by NRHP.

The National Historic Landmark designation is given by the U.S. Department of the Interior to sites which are of exceptional significance to the nation as a whole. Ohio has more than 60 National Historic Landmarks. Houses in Ohio with this designation are specified by NHL.

Ohio's history is reflected through its architecture which is as varied as its builders. Because this is so, an explanation of the development of the architectural styles found in Ohio is included in this guide. Each style is illustrated by a photograph.

Every effort has been made to supply the most current and accurate information. This information was furnished by the house museums themselves. However, we suggest calling the telephone number given for each house before visiting as hours and admission fees may change without notice. Advanced reservations are necessary for group tours.

Most of the buildings included in this guide were private homes. There are several exceptions, however, such as inns and meeting houses. Restored villages have historic homes and other historic buildings listed at the site. Strictly commercial establishments have not been included except for a few inns and taverns of historic significance as a sample of the many interesting buildings with dining facilities in Ohio. The historic houses are generally operated by non-profit organizations.

If any historic house open to the public has inadvertently been omitted from this guide, we welcome further information to include in future revisions.

ACKNOWLEDGEMENTS

Grateful acknowledgement is made to:

The Ohio Historical Society.

The contributing members of The National Society of the Colonial Dames of America in the State of Ohio.

Dr. Compton Allyn, Blair B. Garvey and friends.

DIRECTORY OF HOUSES

PAGE

Indicates site has dining facilities *

DIRECTORY OF HOUSES   PAGE

7

DIRECTORY OF HOUSES   PAGE

8

DIRECTORY OF HOUSES   PAGE

DIRECTORY OF HOUSES　　　　　　　　PAGE

SOME ARCHITECTURAL STYLES IN OHIO

The early settlers of Ohio brought the building traditions of their native eastern seaboard roots with them. Generally, northern Ohio was settled by people from New England and northern New York state, southern Ohio by those from Virginia and the mid-Atlantic states. After the mid-nineteenth century, regional architecture began to lose its prominence. Improved communication and changing construction technology created styles that evolved not from regional considerations but from popular concepts of architecture.

The styles of the houses included in this book are as varied as their builders. It is the sum of the parts which decides the style of a house. No one house has all the elements of any given style. Instead, it is the combination of elements and the form that this combination takes which determines the style.

The following photographs demonstrate the characteristics of each major style found in this book. There are tremendous variations in each style. Regional interpretations of early styles differ in material and execution of stylistic elements. Many of the houses included in this book are not "high style" architect designed buildings but are simple vernacular interpretations of those styles. Vernacular buildings were constructed by local builders to fit a utilitarian need. Sometimes they exhibited features of the current fashionable style.

The style descriptions in this book appear in chronological order of their popularity. It is important to remember that the changes in housing styles follow the same law as the changes in clothing styles, etc. Each new fashion is a reaction to the previous one. Most buildings contain elements of the new and old styles of their era because the process of popularity is ever changing. Also keep in mind the original setting in which the house was built. The surroundings had a significant effect on the design chosen for the house. Where space was available in the country or suburban settings, there was frequently a horizontal emphasis to the design. In the city where space was at a premium, the design remained controlled and vertical. This contrast between urban and rural settings occurs in all styles mentioned in this book. This guide is intended to be only a very general study of Ohio architecture.

by Elisabeth H. Tuttle

ARCHITECTURAL STYLES IN OHIO

Federal — This style was the earliest in Ohio and the one most influenced by regional interpretations. The building shape was generally rectangular or square. Architectural decoration, if any, was in the delicate classical mode. In the northern part of the state this style was frequently built in wood framing while in the south brick predominated. This style was very frequently seen in its vernacular form in the oldest houses of Ohio. The saltbox style, derived from the northern Ohio settlers' New England heritage, was an example of the vernacular interpretation.
Photo by Rita Walsh

Greek Revival — This style was also subject to much regional variation in interpretation and materials. Columns and pilasters (partially attached columns) were the most recognizable features. There were many versions of Greek Revival architecture, however, that did not include these features. The door and window openings had wide horizontal lintels and moldings. Architectural decoration on this style house was heavy and simple. In the northern part of the state the front of the house was often set in the gable end with the roof line creating a classical pediment.
Photo - Ohio Historical Preservation Office

ARCHITECTURAL STYLES IN OHIO

Gothic Revival — The most outstanding features of this style were the steeply pitched end gables. Frequently, a third gable with a pointed arch window was located on the front facade. Elaborate "gingerbread" millwork often decorated the prominent front porch and steep gables.
Photo - Ohio Historic Preservation Office

Italian Villa — The most obvious features of this style were the narrow tower, the bracketed cornice, and the elaborate window heads. This style house was usually built in rural or suburban settings. The irregularity of the design created spaces which were frequently inset with decorative wooden porches.
Photo - Christopher K. Cone.

ARCHITECTURAL STYLES IN OHIO

Italianate — This style shares basic features with the Italian Villa style, although not so elaborate. It usually did not have a tower. It was built most frequently in an urban setting. The shape was generally square or rectangular.

French Second Empire — The most outstanding feature of this style was the large mansard roof with dormer windows. This style appeared with and without a tower.
Photo - Tobias Studio

ARCHITECTURAL STYLES IN OHIO

Queen Anne — The great variety of shapes, textures, and materials was the most outstanding feature of this style of architecture. Towers with various roof styles and very elaborate porches were also important elements. Classically inspired motifs are applied to an almost chaotic combination of color and shape. The emphasis of this design was generally vertical.
Photo by Judy Williams

Shingle — The classical motifs of the Queen Anne style were retained, but the general shape of the building was very different. It became simplified and the emphasis was now on the horizontal rather than the vertical. This was achieved with elongated roof lines and extended porches.
Photo by Stephen Gordon

ARCHITECTURAL STYLES IN OHIO

Richardsonian Romanesque — This style was generally built in stone and was distinguished by its massiveness. A large round tower, heavy classically inspired motifs and rounded arched windows were often features.
Photo by Voris

Colonial Revival — The architecture of colonial America inspired the Colonial Revival, which began in the 1890's and continues today. Often larger in scale than their colonial predecessors, and not always strictly symmetrical, Colonial Revival style buildings have details derived from colonial sources, sometimes used differently from the way they were originally.
Photo by Ted Ligibel

ARCHITECTURAL STYLES IN OHIO

American Foursquare — One of the most common early 20th century building types in Ohio is the American Foursquare, a two-story house with the approximate proportions of a cube and square floor plan. American Foursquares were built in frame, brick, or block, and typically have a one-story porch the width of the front and a hipped roof with a wide overhang. The American Foursquare is a building type rather than an architectural style; many American Foursquares have Arts and Crafts or Colonial Revival style details. The American Foursquare was widely popular from the turn of the 20th century to the 1920's.
Photo by Nancy Recchie

Georgian Revival — The Georgian Revival is similar to the Colonial Revival style, but is based upon 17th and 18th century English prototypes rather than American Colonial architecture. Popular from the 1890's to the present day, Georgian Revival style buildings are almost always symmetrical and are usually built of red brick with classically inspired details of light colored stone or painted wood.
Photo by Diane Freolette

ARCHITECTURAL STYLES IN OHIO

Arts and Crafts — Inspired by a design philosophy rather than architectural style, buildings of the American Arts and Crafts Movement date from the turn of the 20th century to the World War I era and vary widely in appearance. Some of the typical features include the use of natural materials including brick, wood, stone, cement and stucco; battered walls; casement windows; pergolas; and outdoor rooms including living porches, dining porches, and sleeping porches. Interiors often feature beamed ceilings and built-in furnishings, fireplaces with inglenooks, art tile, and art glass.
Photo by Nancy Recchie

Jacobethan — Jacobethan style buildings are almost always masonry with historically accurate details inspired by the English Jacobean and Elizabethan styles. Usually built of fine materials including brick, stone, and copper, the style is one most commonly used for large houses and educational buildings from the turn of the 20th century into the 1930's.
Photo by Ted J. Ligibel

ARCHITECTURAL STYLES IN OHIO

Tudor Revival — Based on 16th century English vernacular architecture, the Tudor Revival style was popular in the U.S. from the 1910's to 1940's, and is especially common in planned suburban communities of the era. The buildings are usually picturesque and asymmetrical, characterized by steep-pitched roofs, tall chimneys, half-timbered walls, and mixed use of brick, stone, and stucco.
Photo by Ted J. Ligibel

French Colonial or Norman Revival — Inspired by the buildings of 16th and 17th century France, the French Colonial or Norman Revival style gained popularity in the U.S. after World War I. Usually brick, stone, and stucco, with steep pitched slate roofs, tall chimneys, occasional half-timbering and casement windows, some examples are picturesque and asymmetrical, while others are formal and symmetrical, recalling French chateaus.
Photo by Patricia J. Forgac

COUNTY MAP OF OHIO

Figures denote the number of historic houses open to the public in each county.

The Index by County starts on page 104.

HISTORIC HOUSES IN OHIO

AKRON

JOHN BROWN HOME, c. 1825; additions
Copley and Diagonal Roads
Akron, Ohio 44320
Summit County
(216) 535-1120

February-December/Tu-Sun/1-5
Closed holidays

Admission fee

This remodeled frame house was the home of the abolitionist, John Brown, who was executed for his 1859 raid at Harper's Ferry, West Virginia. It was named "John Brown Home" to commemorate his two year residency (1844-1846) when he was associated with Colonel Simon Perkins in the sheep and wool business. The building is now a museum containing exhibits. It is included in the guided tour of Perkins Mansion.
Summit County Historical Society

HOWER HOUSE, 1871
60 Fir Hill
Akron, Ohio 44325
Summit County
(216) 375-7460
(216) 972-6909

Guided Tours Wed-Sat/Noon-3:30
Sun/1-4
or by appointment
Closed January and major Holidays

Admission fee

This handsome Second Empire style brick house, with mansard roof, cupola and carved stone lintels was built by John H. Hower, an industrialist. A first floor hexagonal hall is a hub from which five rooms and a stair hall open. Of special interest are the plaster moldings, marble fireplaces and chandeliers. Walnut brought from Michigan was carved on location for the woodwork and stairway to the third floor ballroom and cupola. Occupied for 100 years by one family, the house has furnishings from all over the world. Hower House may be rented by organizations or individuals for social events
NRHP
U. of Akron
Cared for by Victorian Women's Committee
Photo by M.J. Rakas

SIMON PERKINS MANSION, 1835-37

550 Copley Road
Akron, Ohio 44320
Summit County
(216) 535-1120

February-December/Tu-Sun/1-5
Closed holidays

Admission fee

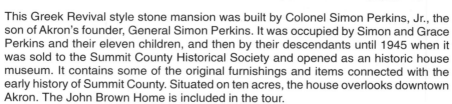

This Greek Revival style stone mansion was built by Colonel Simon Perkins, Jr., the son of Akron's founder, General Simon Perkins. It was occupied by Simon and Grace Perkins and their eleven children, and then by their descendants until 1945 when it was sold to the Summit County Historical Society and opened as an historic house museum. It contains some of the original furnishings and items connected with the early history of Summit County. Situated on ten acres, the house overlooks downtown Akron. The John Brown Home is included in the tour.
NRHP
Summit County Historical Society
Line drawing by Marilyn Griffith

STAN HYWET HALL, 1915

714 N. Portage Path
Akron, Ohio 44303
Summit County
(216) 836-5533

January 24-December
Tu-Sat/10-4/Sun/1-4

Admission fee

Built by Frank A. Seiberling, founder of the Goodyear and Seiberling rubber companies, this 65-room mansion is an excellent example of Tudor Revival architecture. Fascinated by Tudor history, the Seiberlings, their architects and interior designers all visited England to study castles and manor houses before designing the house. The handcrafted woodwork, stonework and molded plaster are noteworthy, as are the fine English and European furnishings which date from the 15th-20th centuries. Guests of the hospitable Seiberling's at Stan Hywet Hall included four presidents, Will Rogers and many artistic performers. There are 70 acres of beautiful gardens, lawns and woods.
NRHP-NHL
Stan Hywet Hall Foundation, Inc.

ALLIANCE

MABLE HARTZELL HISTORICAL HOME, 1867
840 North Park
Alliance, Ohio 44601
Stark County
(216) 821-4256

June-September
Call for summer hours
or by appointment

Admission fee

Matthew and Mary Edwards Earley constructed this fine example of Italianate style architecture. The house is named after the Earley's adopted daughter who willed it to the Alliance Historical Society. The interior has been carefully restored. A stately curved staircase is visible as one enters. In addition to the parlor, sitting room bedrooms etc., there is a trap door concealing back stairs. Many of the rooms have original furnishings including Renaissance Revival and American Eastlake bedroom sets, and the original Italian marble fireplaces.
NRHP
Alliance Historical Society

ASHLAND

ASHLAND COUNTY HISTORICAL MUSEUM, 1859; remodeled
414 Center Street
Ashland, Ohio 44805
Ashland County
(419) 289-3111

April-December
Wed, Fri, Sun/1-4
or by appointment

The Georgian Revival house and carriage house were built by Dr. J.P. Cowan, a physician and U.S. Congressman. In 1906 it was sold to P.A. Myers, one of the founders of F.E. Myers and Bros. Pump Co. Later he gave it to his son, Guy, as a wedding gift. Guy's widow gave it to Ashland College to be used as the home of its president. In 1981 the house became the Ashland County Historical Museum and is located in an Historic District. The house is furnished and has artifacts from the Civil War through World War II, and industrial display and memorabilia from the area. Included in the carriage house are collections of guns, farm implements, and a collection of insects.
NRHP
Ashland County Historical Society

BARNESVILLE

GAY 90's MANSION MUSEUM 1888-1893
532 North Chestnut Street
Barnesville, Ohio 43713
Belmont County
(614) 425-2926

May 1-October 1/Thurs-Sun/1-4:30
Christmas showing by appointment
all December except Christmas Day

Admission fee

A rare example of Richardsonian Romanesque architecture is found in this twenty-six room mansion built by J.W. (Dias) Bradfield. Elegant details of hand carved wood-work, solid brass hardware, molded plaster designs and gold inlaid washbasins are found throughout. Constructed before Barnesville's municipal water system, there are two water tanks on the third floor to provide running water. The third floor ballroom was the scene of many social events at the turn of the century. Appropriate period furnishings decorate the house. The spacious basement contains interesting displays of Americana and a summer kitchen.
NRHP
Belmont County Historical Society, Inc.
Belmont Historical Society photos

BATH

HALE FARM AND VILLAGE, c. 1825-50
2686 Oak Hill Road Box 296
Bath, Ohio 44210
Summit County
(216) 666-3711 or 1-800-589-9703

May-October/Tu-Sat/10-5/Sun/Noon-5
December/Tu-Sun
Closed Mon except Holidays
or by appointment

Admission fee

Hale Farm and Village is an outdoor museum of rural activities and architecture typi-fying an early 19th century settlement in the Western Reserve region. Most of these buildings have been moved to the site, but the Hale family complex was originally here. The *Hale House* (1826), a Federal style brick three-story house, was built by Jonathan Hale, who moved west in 1810. For 15 years a cabin in the wilderness served as home for the Hale family of seven until he built "Old Brick", modeled after memories of his home in Connecticut. Four generations of Hales lived in the house

continued

and it is furnished much as it was during Jonathan's lifetime. It is the focal point of the working historic farm.

Goldsmith House (1827) is one of the finest examples of transition Greek-Federal style architecture in the Western Reserve. It was built by Jonathan Goldsmith, a well-known area architect, for the Robinson family. It was moved to Hale Farm in 1973. The house is well-furnished with lovely period pieces. Upstairs there is an important stencil room with a frieze of 27 eagles and stars indicating the 27 states of the Union at that time. Cooking demonstrations are done in the cellar kitchen. The *Jagger House* (c. 1845), a Greek Revival style house, was built in Bath by Clement Jagger, a prosperous carriage maker. It has been restored and features a stenciled parlor and furnishings of the period. The *Salt Box House* (c. 1830), built in Richfield, has been restored and furnished with simple 19th century country pieces. Other buildings and exhibits open to the public include a barn (1852); a Federal style Law Office (1820); a Greek Revival style Meeting House (1852); a Log Schoolhouse (1816); the *Stow House* (1852), a Greek Revival style house built in Stow and the Land Office (1832). The Grist Mill (1852) has been turned into a carriage museum displaying actual carriages that were used in the Western Reserve.

NRHP
Western Reserve Historical Society

Goldsmith House

BAY VILLAGE

ROSE HILL, 1818, additions
27715 Lake Road
Bay Village, Ohio 44140
Cuyahoga County
(216) 871-7338

March-December/Sun/2-4:30

Joseph Cahoon and his son Joel built this Federal vernacular style farm house in 1818 to replace the log cabin this family of ten had built in 1810 when they were Dover Township's first white settlers. The Cahoons had also previously constructed a gristmill (1813), sawmill and a distillery for peach brandy. The sawmill provided timber for the house. The moldings and sashes were handcrafted. Additions to the house and barn (1882) completed the farm situated along Lake Erie and Cahoon Creek. The last heir left the property to Bay Village in 1917. Restored, after extensive research and renovation, the house contains pioneer relics, Cahoon family Empire and Victorian furnishings, a furnished summer kitchen and a research library for local history and genealogy. The barn serves as a community meeting place.

NRHP

BELLEVUE

HISTORIC LYME VILLAGE, 19th century
S.R. 113 near S.R. 4
Bellevue, Ohio 44811
Huron County
(419) 483-4949

June-August
Guided tours daily except Mon
May and September tours/Sun only

Admission fee

John Wright Mansion

This is a reconstructed village planned to preserve the history of the area. Most of the buildings have been moved to the site. The *John Wright Mansion* (1882), a stately Second-Empire brick mansion, a style usually found in an urban area, was built here by John Wright as a farm house. When a young English immigrant, Wright dreamed of owning land and a gracious home. To construct it in his sixtieth year he had built on his property a saw mill, kiln, mill and barns. Of special interest are the graceful stairway and third floor ballroom with a stage under the central tower. The house serves the village as a museum with exhibit rooms, dining area and office. Other buildings include the *Seymour House Museum* (1836); *Annie Brown Log House* (1851); *Wagner and Schriner Log Houses;* Groton Postmark Research Center which contains the National Postmark Collectors Club collections; Biebricher Centennial Barn (1876) and Blacksmith Shop; Merry School House; Detterman Log Church; Kromer Barn; Shugh Hardware; and Carriage House Cafe.
NRHP
Historic Lyme Village Association

BEREA

MAHLER MUSEUM, 1854
118 E. Bridge Street
Berea, Ohio 44017
Cuyahoga County
(216) 243-2541

May-December/Sun & Tu/2-4
or by appointment

Donation

This simple Italianate Renaissance style house was built of Berea sandstone. It features mid-Victorian era furnishings and early Berea memorabilia. A newly added educational wing called the History Center features special historical exhibits.
NRHP
Berea Historical Society
Photo by Henry M. Barr Studios, Inc.

BEVERLY

OLIVER TUCKER MUSEUM, 1835
Park and Fifth Street
Beverly, Ohio 45715
Washington County
(614) 984-2489

**June-August/Sat, Sun/1-4
or by appointment**

Donation

A New England Gingerbread style home with a slate roof, this two-story dwelling was built by John Dodge as a wedding gift for his daughter, Corrine Patterson. Several owners later, Beverly's first hardware and general store owner, Oliver Tucker, resided here. Goods for his store and furnishings for his home came by sternwheeler from Pittsburgh. His daughters were the area's first college (Vassar) graduates. A granddaughter gave the home to the Lower Muskingum Historical Society for a museum. It presently has early furniture, tools and pictures on display. Next door is an older log house which has been moved from Waterford.
Lower Muskingum Historical Society

BRECKSVILLE

SQUIRE RICH HOUSE MUSEUM, 1840
9367 Brecksville Road
Brecksville, Ohio 44141
Cuyahoga County
(216) 526-7165

**May-October/Sun/2-5
or by appointment
Tour Groups welcome**

The salt box style house was erected by Brecksville farmer and Justice of the Peace Squire Charles B. Rich. All wood for the house including the ash floors, the black walnut woodwork and the doors came from trees on the property. A local sawmill powered by nearby Chippewa Creek prepared the wood for the house. The house has been fully restored and is decorated and furnished as a typical Brecksville residence might have been during the 1860's.
NRHP
Brecksville Historical Association, Inc.
Cleveland Metroparks System

BROOKVILLE

SAMUEL SPITLER HOUSE, 1894
14 Market Street
Brookville, Ohio 45309
Montgomery County
(513) 833-3470 or (513) 833-2261

**January-December/Sat, Sun/1-5
or by appointment
Closed holidays**

Admission fee

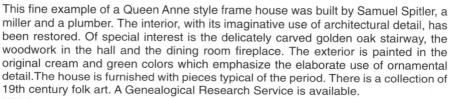

This fine example of a Queen Anne style frame house was built by Samuel Spitler, a miller and a plumber. The interior, with its imaginative use of architectural detail, has been restored. Of special interest is the delicately carved golden oak stairway, the woodwork in the hall and the dining room fireplace. The exterior is painted in the original cream and green colors which emphasize the elaborate use of ornamental detail.The house is furnished with pieces typical of the period. There is a collection of 19th century folk art. A Genealogical Research Service is available.
NRHP
Brookville Historical Society, Inc.

BURTON

CENTURY VILLAGE, 19th century
14653 East Park Street
Burton, Ohio 44021
Geauga County
(216) 834-4012

**June-October/Wed-Sun/1-5
Tours Tu-Sat/10:30, 1, 3/Sun 1, 3**

Admission fee

Hickox Brick House

Century Village is a re-creation of a 19th century Western Reserve Village. The buildings were moved to the site, except for the Federal style *Hickox Brick House* (1838; 1848) NRHP. Built by Eleazer and Stella Hickox, whose father, Thomas Umberfield, settled in Burton in 1798. The frame addition is part of his first home and its interior shows an early 19th century one-room house. The Greek Revival style *Boughton House* (1834), built by George Boughton has been restored and is furnished in the 1820-1840 period. The Federal style *William Law House* (1817) is furnished in the 1810-1840 country period. The *Peter Hitchcock House* (1824) was built by this Ohio Supreme Court Justice. The New England style doorway is original to the house. The *Cook House* (1806), built by Marimom Cook is the oldest farm house in Geauga County and is furnished in the period. For years it was known as the Missionary House because of church meetings held there. Other buildings with exhibits include The Ladies Friend Dressmaking Shop, The White Barn (c.1840), a blacksmith shop (1822), a school house (1872), The Red Barn (1865), a church (1846), a railroad station, caboose.
Geauga County Historical Society

CAMP DENNISON

CHRISTIAN WALDSCHMIDT HOUSE, 1804
7567 Glendale-Milford Road (S.R. 126)
Camp Dennison, Ohio 45111
Hamilton County
(513) 821-0555

**First Sun in May through last Sun in October/1-5
or by appointment**

Donation

This Pennsylvania Dutch style house was constructed of fieldstone and white mortar after the style of the Pennsylvania countryside where Christian Waldschmidt and some of his family had once lived. He and several other families crossed the Allegheny Mountains and settled in New Germany near the Little Miami River. He established the first paper mill in Ohio. The house was used as General Joshua Bate's Headquarters during the Civil War, and the area became known as Camp Dennison. In 1941, the house was purchased by Mr. and Mrs. Chester Kroger, who presented it and the surrounding land to the Daughters of the American Revolution. The DAR restored it and furnished it with family pieces dating before 1840. Civil War and historical relics are on display.
NRHP
Ohio Society Daughters of the American Revolution

CANAL FULTON

OBERLIN HOUSE c. 1847; additions
225 Cherry Street
Canal Fulton, Ohio 44614
Stark County
(216) 854-3808

**June-August/Sun/1-4
or by appointment**

Admission fee

At one time, this saltbox style frame house was occupied by Christopher and Sarah Oberlin, grandparents of Gladys Burgert Mitchell who was born in the house and who donated it to the Heritage Society. Of special interest is the "borning room". Many pieces of furniture and Americana have been donated to the house which is located in the Canal Fulton Historic District.
NRHP
Canal Fulton Heritage Society
Photo by Wolfgang Weber

CANFIELD

LOGHURST, 1803; addition
3967 Broadman-Canfield Road, S.R. 224
Canfield, Ohio 44406
Mahoning County
(216) 533-4330

**May-October 31, December/Tu-Sat/10-5
Sunday, holidays/Noon-5
April, November and
group tours by appointment**

Admission fee

Located in Mahoning County, Loghurst Farm is possibly the oldest and largest remaining dwelling in the Western Reserve. Built in 1805, this three-story log structure was enlarged around 1827. A frame addition which houses a kitchen designed to facilitate its increasing success as an inn and stagecoach stop was built. Throughout its history, Loghurst remained a well-known fixture in its community, not only for its prominence as a family farm and business, but also as a station on the Underground Railroad. First floor rooms have been restored to late 19th early 20th century appearance, while interpretation covers the house's entire history. Of additional interest are a carriage house display of turn of the century farm machinery and some small livestock. The museum is also open for special group or school tours, and its restored kitchen is available for meetings or use as a classroom facility.
Western Reserve Historical Society

CARROLLTON

McCOOK HOUSE, 1837
Public Square
Carrollton, Ohio 44615
Carroll County
(216) 627-5559

**June-October/Fri-Sat/9-5
Sun and July 4th/1-5
or by appointment**

Admission fee

Major Daniel McCook, a lawyer by profession, built this large Federal style brick house on the public square. It is known as the "Fighting McCook House" because Major McCook, his nine sons and five nephews had distinguished service in the military during the Mexican and Civil Wars. They also had prominent careers as civilians. The house was acquired by the State of Ohio in 1941 and dedicated in 1948 as a memorial to the gallant "Fighting McCooks". It is partially furnished with period pieces and some of the house is devoted to memorabilia of the McCook family and the Civil War.
NRHP
Ohio Historical Society
Carroll County Historical Society

CELINA

RILEY HOME, 1896
Mercer County Historical Museum
130 East Market Street
Celina, Ohio 45882
Mercer County
(419) 586-6065

January-December/Wed-Fri/8:30-4
October-April/Wed-Fri/8:30-4/Sun/1-4

Calvin E. Riley, a commercial bank president, built this Victorian home which was lived in by three generations of his family. The interior decor of the 19th century home is enlivened by the rich history and adventures of the family. The entrance, crafted of oak with a parquet floor is reminiscent of the ship's cabin of his seafaring grandfather, Captain James Riley whose portrait greets you. A world traveler and author, Captain Riley and his son, James Watson, surveyed the old Northwest Territory beginning in 1819. Calvin's son, James Zura, traveled to the gold fields of Alaska. Now a museum, the house is filled with numerous displays reflecting life in the area over the past two centuries. Kitchen utensils, carpenter tools, items from a general store, medical equipment and Indian artifacts are also exhibited.
NRHP
Mercer County Historical Society

CENTERVILLE

WALTON HOUSE, c. 1838; additions
89 West Franklin Street
Centerville, Ohio 45459
Montgomery County
(513) 433-0123

January-December/Th/1-5/Sat/12-4
or by appointment

Donation

This Federal building follows the Virginia style cottage plan with double front doors and fireplaces in the gable ends. Its history dates back to 1838 when it was built by Henry Reese as a two-room stone cottage with a loft. After a succession of owners, as well as additions and changes, it was purchased by William and Miriam Walton who maintained it for forty-four years. Their heirs presented the cottage and its contents to the Centerville Historical Society in 1971. Following restoration, the house closely resembles its original design. It now serves as the headquarters for the Historical Society and a museum which contains a collection of local memorabilia.
NRHP
Centerville Historical Society

CHILLICOTHE

ADENA, 1807

Off Adena Road, West of S.R. 104
Chillicothe, Ohio 45601
Ross County
(614) 772-1500

Memorial Day-Labor Day
Wed-Sat/9:30-5/Sun/Noon-5
September, October/Weekends

Admission fee

Adena is one of the Midwest's finest early houses. It was built by Thomas Worthington, a founding father of the State of Ohio. Worthington was one of the state's first U.S. Senators and its sixth governor. Benjamin Lathrobe assisted in the design of the elegant, modified Georgian, sandstone mansion which is situated on a hilltop overlooking the Chillicothe area with a view of the scene on the Great Seal of the State of Ohio. The house is beautifully furnished with Sheraton and Hepplewhite pieces and family heirlooms. There are outbuildings and formal gardens on the spacious grounds.
NRHP
Ohio Historical Society - OHS Photo

MARIANNE AND CHARLES FRANKLIN HOUSE, c. 1900

80 South Paint Street
Chillicothe, Ohio 45601
Ross County
(614) 772-1936

April 1-November 30/Tu-Sun/1-5
December 1-March 31/Sat and Sun/1-5
Last tour starts at 4:00 p.m.

Admission fee

Since 1900, this American Foursquare style house was the residence of Marianne and Charles Franklin. In 1973, the Ross County Historical Society opened it as a museum dedicated primarily to the women of Ross County and their part in its history. The displays feature antiques, glass, clothing and products of women's activities from pioneer days to the present.
NRHP
Ross County Historical Society

LUCY HAYES BIRTHPLACE, c. 1825

90 West Sixth Street
Chillicothe, Ohio 45601
Ross County
(614) 775-LUCY (5829)

Appointment only

Donations

This classic Federal birthplace of "Lemonade Lucy" in 1831 was saved from demolition in 1968. Lucy Ware Webb Hayes was the first presidential wife to be called "The First Lady of Our Land", following her husband's 1877 inauguration as the 19th President of the United States. The first presidential wife in the White House with a college degree, Lucy was considered the leader of "The New Woman Era". While caring for soldiers during the Civil War she was fondly called "Mother Lucy". This simple two over two house shows living heritage displays. There are costumes, interpretive actors live and on film, and music and videos of Lucy's Era (1831 to 1889).
NRHP
Scioto Valley Arts Council

KNOLES LOG HOUSE, 1800-1825

39 West Fifth Street
Chillicothe, Ohio 45601
Ross County
(614) 772-1936

April-November/Tu-Sun/1-5
December-March/Sat and Sun/1-5
Last tour starts at 4:00 p.m.

Admission fee

The Knoles Log House was built in the 1800's as a two-story simple log house and was purchased in 1835 by William Knoles, a farmer and business man in Chillicothe. It was moved to its present location in 1990. Featured in this log house are period furnishings, an herb garden and early household utensils and tools. During the year there are seasonal on site demonstrations including open hearth cooking, arts and crafts, and frontier type activities. The Knoles House illustrates how people who came to Chillicothe in the 1800's lived.
Ross County Historical Society

DAVID McCANDLESS McKELL LIBRARY, 1838

39 West Fifth Street
Chillicothe, Ohio 45601
Ross County
(614) 773-1896

January-December
Tu, Wed, Fri and Sat/1-5

Admission fee

This Classic Revival style building was given to the Ross County Historical Society by Colonel David McKell. It houses displays of rare and historic books and art collections. The library now has over 10,000 books and pamphlets in its catalog on a wide range of subjects. A reference library is available for students.
NRHP
Ross County Historical Society

ROSS COUNTY HISTORICAL SOCIETY MUSEUM, 1838

45 West Fifth Street
Chillicothe, Ohio 45601
Ross County
(614) 772-1936

April 1-November 30/Tu-Sun/1-5
December 1-March 31/Sat and Sun/1-5
Last tour starts at 4:00 p.m.

Admission fee

This house was the former residence of the William T. McClintock family, various politicians and a pioneer judge. It is now operated as a historical museum and contains archeological artifacts, furniture, toys, tools, Civil War Room and a Northwest Territory exhibit. The Constitution Room contains the table on which the Constitution of the State of Ohio was written and signed. This table is a reminder of when Chillicothe was the first Territorial Capital of the Northwest Territory and later (1803-1816) capital of the State of Ohio.
NRHP
Ross County Historical Society
Photo by Charles E. Tomastik

CINCINNATI

THE WILLIAM BETTS HOUSE, 1804
The Betts House Research Center
416 Clark Street
Cincinnati, Ohio 45203
Hamilton County
(513) 651-0734

**January-December/Tu, Thurs/10-4
or by appointment
Closed major holidays**

The two story Federal style brick house was built by William and Phoebe Stevens Betts. Betts, a New Jersey native, brought his family to Cincinnati in 1800 where he established a brick yard. He also farmed the 111 acres he acquired and on which he built the house. The house, now surrounded by urban development, stands just west of Music Hall. In 1990 the house was saved from total decay by a partnership formed by the descendants of William and Phoebe Betts and interested friends of the partners. In 1995 the partnership made a gift of the house to The National Society of the Colonial Dames of America in the State of Ohio. It is now the Betts House Research Center, whose mission is the interpretation of the history of Cincinnati from 1800 to the present through the study of the evolution of building materials over that time period.
The National Society of the Colonial Dames of America in the State of Ohio

CARY COTTAGE, 1832
7000 Hamilton Avenue
Cincinnati, Ohio 45231
Hamilton County
(513) 522-3860

**January-December/first Sun each month/1-4
Weekdays by appointment**

Alice and Phobe Cary, mid-19th century poets, lived in this Federal vernacular style brick house from 1832, when it was completed, to 1850 when they went to New York to become internationally recognized writers. Built by their father, Robert Cary, the house has been restored and furnished in the style of the early 19th century and contains some family possessions. One room, with period furnishings and artifacts dating after 1850, is dedicated to the founders of the Clovernook Center on whose grounds this house stands.
NRHP
The Clovernook Center—Opportunities for the Blind

JOHN HAUCK HOUSE, 1870

812 Dayton Street
Cincinnati, Ohio 45214
Hamilton County
(513) 721-4506

January-December/Thur/10-4
Fri/11-3/ Sun/1-5
Open December
special hours-daily except Monday

Admission fee

This ornate Italianate townhouse with dressed stone facade and carriage house was built by George Skaats, a wealthy coal dealer, city alderman and Ohio representative. A decade later John Hauck, a German immigrant and owner of a Cincinnati brewery, purchased the home and completed it. The house has spacious rooms and intricately painted ceilings, floors of parqueted wood in elaborate patterns, marble mantels and massive woodwork. Both floors are furnished with pieces that reflect the elegant, late Victorian lifestyle of a wealthy and prominent family. Dayton Street was once known as "Millionaires Row" because so many prominent industrialists lived in its fine townhouses.
NRHP
Historic Southwest Ohio, Inc.

MILLER-LEUSER LOG HOUSE, 1796, addition

6540 Clough Pike
Cincinnati, Ohio 45244
Hamilton County
Mailing Address:
P.O. Box 30174
Cincinnati, Ohio 45230
(513) 231-2114

By appointment

Typical of the earliest permanent houses in Ohio, this log structure derives its name from the pioneer builder, Icabod Benton Miller and the last owners, the Lawrence Leuser family. It was built in 1796 on the present site and lived in continuously until purchased by the Anderson Township Historical Society in 1971. It was never modernized except for a few electric lights. Presently, the house is used as a teaching museum with emphasis on the Ohio frontier. A barn and other outbuildings are part of the exhibits of the 19th century period. The Society maintains a history museum and library in an adjacent building with emphasis on the history of Anderson Township, Hamilton County, Ohio.
NRHP
Anderson Township Historical Society

PETERLOON, 1929-1930

8605 Hopewell Road
Cincinnati, Ohio 45242
Hamilton County
(513) 791-7600

By appointment

Admission fee

Mr. and Mrs. John J. Emery engaged architect William A. Delano to design this
stately Georgian style home. Mr. Emery
was an industrialist, philanthropist, cultural
and civic leader in Cincinnati. His wife,
Irene, was the daughter of artist Charles
Dana Gibson and a niece of Nancy Langhorne, Lady Astor. Of special interest are the
paneled rooms that date to the period of Charles II, parquet floors and eclectic antique furnishings. The house is surrounded by yew and boxwood gardens, terraces
and gravel walkways. In 1979 the house and 71 acres were placed in a Foundation
that opens Peterloon to the public. Tours and social events may be scheduled by
charitable, non-profit groups.
Peterloon Foundation

HARRIET BEECHER STOWE HOUSE, c. 1832; additions

2950 Gilbert Avenue
Cincinnati, Ohio 45206
Hamilton County
(513) 632-5120

January-December/Tu-Th/10-4

From 1832-1850, this two-story house was the home of Dr. Lyman Beecher, a Pres-
byterian minister and president of Lane Theological Seminary. His daughter, Harriet
Beecher Stowe, was the author of *Uncle Tom's Cabin.* The house is now a museum
with one room devoted to the Beecher family. The other rooms concentrate on exhibits showing African-American history. Stowe House serves as a meeting place for
community groups and houses C.C.Y.'s Educational Center.
NRHP
Ohio Historical Society
Citizen's Committee on Youth

TAFT MUSEUM, c. 1820

316 Pike Street
Cincinnati, Ohio 45202
Hamilton County
(513) 241-0343

January-December
Mon-Sat/10-5
Sun/holidays/1-5
Closed Thanksgiving,
Christmas and New Year's Day

The Taft Museum is an excellent example of an historic mansion converted into a museum. It is one of the finest Federal houses in the Midwest. It was built facing Lytle Park in what is now downtown Cincinnati for Martin Baum, a wealthy entrepreneur. Nicholas Longworth, David Sinton and Mr. and Mrs. Charles Phelps Taft were subsequent owners. The Tafts decorated their home with one of America's finest private art collections and then gave the house and its contents to the city in 1931. It opened as a public museum in 1932 and enjoys a world wide reputation. Paintings include works by Rembrandt, Gainsborough, Hals, Ingres, Reynolds, Turner, Corot, Sargent and others. French Renaissance painted enamels, Chinese porcelains, and Duncan Phyfe period furniture are included in the permanent collection. The museum also displays changing special exhibitions throughout the year. A formal garden is situated on the southeast side.
NRHP-NHL
Cincinnati Institute of Fine Arts
Photo by Tony Walsh for Taft Museum

WILLIAM HOWARD TAFT NATIONAL HISTORIC SITE, 1840; 1852

2038 Auburn Avenue
Cincinnati, Ohio 45219
Hamilton County
(513) 684-3262

Daily 10-4/closed Thanksgiving,
Christmas & New Years's Day

The Greek Revival Style brick Taft House was the birthplace and boyhood home of William Howard Taft, President of the United States from 1909 to 1913, and Chief Justice of the Supreme Court from 1921 to 1930. His father, Alphonso Taft, was a prominent lawyer and judge. Under President Grant, he served as Secretary of War, Attorney General and later as Minister to Austria and then Minister to Russia. The house is simple in design. An interesting cornice gives it an Italianate style feeling.
NRHP-NHL
The National Park Service

CLEVELAND

DUNHAM TAVERN MUSEUM, 1824-1825
6709 Euclid Avenue
Cleveland, Ohio 44103
Cuyahoga County
(216) 431-1060

January-December/Tours Wed and Sun/1-4
Group tours by appointment
Closed holidays

Admission fee

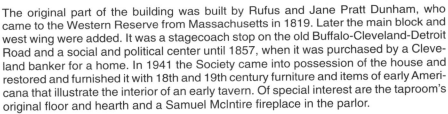

The original part of the building was built by Rufus and Jane Pratt Dunham, who came to the Western Reserve from Massachusetts in 1819. Later the main block and west wing were added. It was a stagecoach stop on the old Buffalo-Cleveland-Detroit Road and a social and political center until 1857, when it was purchased by a Cleveland banker for a home. In 1941 the Society came into possession of the house and restored and furnished it with 18th and 19th century furniture and items of early Americana that illustrate the interior of an early tavern. Of special interest are the taproom's original floor and hearth and a Samuel McIntire fireplace in the parlor.
NRHP
Dunham Tavern Museum

WESTERN RESERVE HISTORICAL SOCIETY
10825 East Boulevard
University Circle
Cleveland, Ohio 44106
Cuyahoga County
(216) 721-5722

January-December/Tu-Sat/10-5
Sun/Noon-5

Admission fee

HAY-McKINNEY MANSION - 1908-1911

BINGHAM-HANNA MANSION - 1916-1919

Built as private homes these two Italian Renaissance buildings on East Boulevard, joined together by the Norton Central Addition, make up the Western Reserve Historical Society complex. Each was a three story mansion of masonry construction and reflected the style of a Florentine country villa with extensive formal gardens. They were among the most impressive homes in the fashionable area adjoining 73 acre Wade Park during the early years of the 20th century. The beautiful furnishings reflect the desire of wealthy American industrialists of the era to import European culture to create sophisticated homes. The *Hay-McKinney Mansion* was built by Mrs. John Hay, widow of the distinguished author and diplomat who served as Secretary of State in the McKinley and Roosevelt administrations. She selected Abram Garfield, son of the

continued

martyred president, as her architect to plan a building of great simplicity and dignity. The interior rooms open from a large entrance hall, the main feature of which is a long carved staircase. It was carved in 1875 by famous interior woodcarver, John Herkomer, for the Euclid Avenue home in which Mrs. Hay had been raised. In 1916 the mansion was bought by Price McKinney who furnished it with many beautiful antiques he brought from Europe. In 1938 the Historical Society purchased the mansion and made it a museum. NRHP. The *Bingham-Hanna Mansion* was built by Harry Payne Bingham, a member of one of Cleveland's most prominent families. The architects were the nationally known firm of Walker and Gillette. The interior of this home contains paneled wood ceilings painted with 16th century designs, massive stone fireplaces and thick walnut doors and a formal U-shaped staircase with a wide landing framed by massive columns. In 1920 the Bingham Mansion was purchased by Mrs. Leonard Colton Hanna, widow of the president of the M.A. Hanna Company, who furnished the house with great art treasures, including fine tapestries. Mrs. Hanna lived in her home until her death in 1936 when it was acquired by the Historical Society.
NRHP
Western Reserve Historical Society
WRHS photo

COLUMBUS

HERITAGE MUSEUM OF KAPPA KAPPA GAMMA, 1852; addition
530 East Town Street, Box 38
Columbus, Ohio 43215
Franklin County
(614) 228-6515

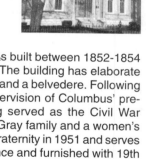

January-December/Mon-Fri/10-4
Docent tours
weekend dates by appointment

Admission fee

This fine example of the Renaissance Italian Villa style was built between 1852-1854 by Philip T. Snowden, a prosperous dry goods merchant. The building has elaborate carved window and door surrounds, a wide paneled frieze and a belvedere. Following a fire in 1872, the building was remodeled under the supervision of Columbus' premier 19th century architect George Bellows Sr. Having served as the Civil War governor's mansion, the home of the prominent David S. Gray family and a women's club, the house was purchased by Kappa Kappa Gamma Fraternity in 1951 and serves as its national headquarters. Restored to its former elegance and furnished with 19th century furniture, the period museum rooms provide a handsome setting for the display of fraternity memorabilia as well as for interpretations of women's culture.
NRHP
Kappa Kappa Gamma Fraternity

KELTON HOUSE, 1852

586 East Town Street
Columbus, Ohio 43215
Franklin County
(614) 464-2022

January-December/Sun 1-4
closed holiday weekends

Admission fee

This house was built for Fernando Cortex Kelton, a prominent Columbus merchant whose family occupied the home 123 years. The exterior design is Greek Revival, while the interior reflects the Victorian period. The museum portion of the house contains twin parlors, sitting room, dining room and two bedrooms. The Kelton family furniture and the memorabilia spanning three generations reflect the urban lifestyle of the last half of the 19th century. The house was once a station on the Underground Railroad. The attached Carriage House and lower level rooms are available for community meetings and social gatherings. A project of the Junior League of Columbus, this house is in a National Historic District.
NRHP
Junior League of Columbus, Inc.

THURBER HOUSE, c. 1873

77 Jefferson Avenue
Columbus, Ohio 43215
Franklin County
(614) 464-1032

Open daily Noon-4
Guided tours available for a fee
some Sundays or by appointment

Thurber House is a two and a half story red brick Queen Anne style home that is significant for its affiliation with Columbus' native son and one of America's best known humorist/cartoonists, James Thurber. It contains some of his memorabilia and drawings from his career with the New Yorker Magazine. The house was restored in 1984 to the nineteens period when it was occupied by Mr. and Mrs. Charles Thurber and their three sons. The covered gable roof is intact and ornamental wooden porches grace the front and back of the house. The house currently functions as an active literary center.
NRHP
Jefferson Center for Learning and the Arts

COSHOCTON

POMERENE CENTER FOR THE ARTS
JOHNSON-HUMRICKHOUSE HOME, 1834
302 S. Third Street at Mulberry
Coshocton, Ohio 43812
Coshocton County
(614) 622-0326

Tues-Sat/1-4

This Greek Revival style house was built by George Silliman, husband of Ann Johnson. The Johnson and Humrickhouse families were early settlers in the area and the children inter-married. Two Johnson brothers were world travelers and the artifacts they amassed are in the Johnson Humrickhouse Museum in Roscoe Village. The house was later owned by the Pomerene family. They donated the house to the village of Coshocton as an art center/gallery. A wide pillared porch across the front of the house, the twelve foot ceilings, hand carved window cornices and landscaped grounds are noteworthy.
NRHP
Pomerene Center for the Arts

ROSCOE VILLAGE, 1830-1860s
381 Hill Street
Coshocton, Ohio 43812
Coshocton County
(614) 622-9310 or 1-800-877-1830

April-December/Daily/ 11-5
Limited schedule remainder of the year
Closed New Year's Day,
Thanksgiving, Christmas

Admission to the Village is free
A ticket is required to enter some buildings

Roscoe Village is a restoration of a canal town that thrived from 1830-1860's on the Ohio and Erie Canal. Most of the brick and frame structures in the Village are on their original sites. The *Dr. Maro Johnson House* was built in 1833 and is of the basic Greek Revival architecture with its rectangular shape, stone lentils at the windows and doors, and window lights above the front entrance. The four-story home has one floor below street level which opens onto the canal bank. Here is where the kitchen and pantry are located. These rooms have hand-chiseled sandstone walls and brick floors. The doctor's study, parlor and dining room are accessible from the street level. The furnishings are of the period. Two bedrooms and a nursery are located on the third floor. Restoration was begun in 1971 with very few alterations. The gardens behind the house represent the style of the gardens and plant materials used during the canal era. Dr. Maro Johnson, doctor in Roscoe from 1833-83, purchased the home in 1841. He built the small white building in 1842 as an office. NRHP

continued

The Toll House (c. 1840). This home of Roscoe's first toll collector, Jacob Welsh, was constructed of bricks made in Roscoe. Greek Revival in design, it has stepped gables that show the Dutch influence. In this house canal boats were registered and tolls were collected. NRHP. *The Craftsman House* (Daniel Boyd House) was built in 1833. The one-room home is furnished to the period and is an excellent example of early family living space. The weaving room would have been a lean-to and contains two looms, one of which could be taken apart and transported from place to place.
Roscoe Village Foundation
Photos courtesy of the Roscoe Village Foundation

The Craftsman House

DAYTON

CARILLON HISTORICAL PARK
2001 S. Patterson Blvd.
Exit 51 off I-75
Dayton, Ohio 45409
Montgomery County
(513) 293-2841
Exit 51 off 1-75

May-October/Tu-Sat/10-6/Sun/1-6

Admission fee

Carillon Historical Park concentrates on the settlement of the Miami Valley, its early transportation, and local industry and invention. Among the many buildings on the 65-acre site are two historic homes which have been moved to the site and restored. *Newcom Tavern* (1796) a two-story log house, was built for Colonel George Newcom, a Dayton pioneer. Dayton's oldest building, the tavern has served as a courthouse, store, school, church, and post office as well as an inn and home. *William Morris House* (c. 1815), built of locally quarried limestone, was once located in rural Washington Township. Both homes contain period furnishings. Other historic buildings include an 1896 one-room school, an 1894 railway station, an 1885 canal superintendent's office and a 1909 railroad watchtower.
Carillon Historical Park, Inc.
Photo courtesy of Carillon Historical Park, Inc.

CARRIAGE HILL METRO PARK FARM, 1836/1878

7800 E. Shull Rd.
1 mile north of I-70 on E. Shull Rd.
Dayton, Ohio 45424
Montgomery County
(513) 879-0461

January-December/Mon-Fri/10-5
Sat, Sun, holidays/1-5
Closed Christmas and New Year's Day

The Carriage Hill Metro Park Farm House is a Federal vernacular brick farmhouse with simple interiors and furnishings. Five generations of Arnolds, German Baptists, built maintained and shared in the prosperity of the homestead. Today, the homestead, a working farm, is a living historical museum. The farm includes three homes, two barns, blacksmith and woodworking shops, related outbuildings and the family cemetery. During weekdays, the buildings are open for viewing and the house is interpreted by a historical homemaker. Each Saturday and Sunday, volunteers interpret the homestead farm. Special programs recreating the lifestyle of a conservative farm family of the 1880's are presented each Sunday. These programs follow the seasonal activities as related to the farm. A children's interactive area and country store are housed in the visitors center.
NRHP
Park District Dayton-Montgomery County

DUNBAR HOUSE, c. 1890

219 N. Summit Street
Dayton, Ohio 45407
Montgomery County
(513) 224-7061

Memorial Day-Labor Day/Wed-Sat/9:30-5
Sun & holidays/Noon-5
September-October/Weekends
Other times by appointment

Admission fee

This late Victorian style brick house purchased for his mother, was the home of Paul Lawrence Dunbar from 1898 until his death in 1906. The son of former slaves, he is known as the "poet-laureate of the Negro race" and was the first Black American writer to achieve international recognition. The house is furnished and contains Dunbar family belongings and artifacts. This property is a State Memorial.
NRHP-NHL
Ohio Historical Society - OHS Photo

PATTERSON HOMESTEAD, 1816
1815 Brown Street
Dayton, Ohio 45409
Montgomery County
(513) 222-9724 or (513) 228-6271

April-December/Tu-Fri/10-4/Sun/1-4
January-March by appointment

The Patterson Homestead was built by Colonel Robert Patterson on a 700 acre tract. The rambling Federal style brick house was lived in by three generations of Pattersons. Two of his grandchildren, John H. and Frank Patterson founded the National Cash Register Company. Colonel Patterson was born in Bedford County, Pennsylvania in 1753. He fought in the Revolutionary War. He was a veteran of numerous Indian wars in both Kentucky and Ohio. After he moved to Ohio, he was commissioned a Quartermaster in the War of 1812. Following the Treaty of Ghent in 1814, he built the homestead to replace the log house he and his family had occupied since 1804. The house is furnished with antiques and tours are given by trained guides. A meeting house is available for the use of non-profit organizations.
NRHP
Owned and maintained by the City of Dayton
Administered by Montgomery County Historical Society

DELAWARE

NASH HOUSE, 1876; addition
157 East William Street (S.R. 42)
Delaware, Ohio 43015
Delaware County
(614) 369-3831
March-November 15/Sun, Wed/2-4:30/Thurs/9:30-11:45 and 1-4:30

This two-story red brick Italianate house built by John Slattery was purchased by William Henry Nash in 1885 and later willed to his son, Eugene P. Nash. His daughter, Pauline Nash, gave the house to the Delaware County Historical Society in 1954. It is furnished as a home of the mid 19th century with many interesting period pieces. The collection features walnut furniture carved by John Robinson, who emigrated to Delaware County from England in 1833. In addition, memorabilia of Rutherford B. Hayes, 19th President of the United States, born in Delaware in 1822, is located in the house along with personal items of Frank B. Willis, 45th Governor of Ohio, who was born in Delaware County. There is a museum connected with the house that contains a collection of Delaware rocking chairs made in a local factory, memorabilia from various American wars, as well as historical items of interest and a genealogy and local history library.
Delaware County Historical Society

DOVER

JEREMIAH E. REEVES HOME, late 19th century

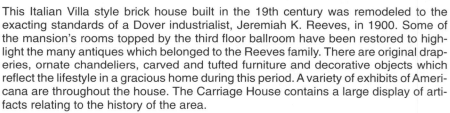

325 E. Iron Avenue
Dover, Ohio 44622
Tuscarawas County
(216) 343-7040

Mid-May to mid-September/10-4
First 2 weeks December/2-8 daily

Admission fee

This Italian Villa style brick house built in the 19th century was remodeled to the exacting standards of a Dover industrialist, Jeremiah K. Reeves, in 1900. Some of the mansion's rooms topped by the third floor ballroom have been restored to highlight the many antiques which belonged to the Reeves family. There are original draperies, ornate chandeliers, carved and tufted furniture and decorative objects which reflect the lifestyle in a gracious home during this period. A variety of exhibits of Americana are throughout the house. The Carriage House contains a large display of artifacts relating to the history of the area.
NRHP
Dover Historical Society

EAST LIVERPOOL

C.C. THOMPSON HOME, 1876; addition

305 Walnut Street
East Liverpool, Ohio 43920
Columbiana County
(216) 385-2550 or (216) 386-5964

By appointment

Donation

Pottery owner Cassius C. Thompson built this fine Italian villa style home with its two-story tower. Construction materials included stone and unglazed brick now painted in a typical Victorian color scheme. The new "bathroom addition" was built in 1900. The double entrance doors contain etched glass panels and the inner doors feature red glass. The central oval stairwell of local black walnut extends to the third floor. The home is fully furnished with the majority of the pieces original to the Thompson family. The home was donated to the East Liverpool Historical Society by C.C.'s son, Dale. An ongoing restoration is seeking to recreate the 1900 appearance of the house.
NRHP
East Liverpool Historical Society

EATON

PREBLE COUNTY HISTORICAL CENTER

7693 Swartsel Road
Eaton, Ohio 45320
Preble County
(513) 787-4256

April-October, December
first Sun each month/1-5
or by appointment

The Preble County Historical Farm Center is committed to preservation, conservation of land, and wildlife and educational programs. Within The Center are two historic houses: the *Lewisburg Log House* (c. 1800-1825) was dismantled and moved to The Center from Lewisburg. The first recorded occupant was Henry Horn a founder of Lewisburg in 1818 and a blacksmith. Horn owned and operated several mills, a still house and tannery. It houses the Society's pre-1840 period artifacts. The *Sayler-Swartsel House* (c. 1860) reflects the influence of both the Greek and Gothic Revival styles. It was built by Mr. and Mrs. Sebastian Sayler, and the last occupants were the Swartsel family. Numerous additions and alterations have been made through the years. It now houses part of the Society's collection of textiles and household items.
Preble County Historical Society
Photo courtesy of Ball Publishing Co.

ELYRIA

THE HICKORIES, 1894

509 Washington Avenue
Elyria, Ohio 44035
Lorain County
(216) 322-3341

January-December/Wed-Fri/1-4
or by appointment

Admission fee

Arthur Lovett Garford, a prosperous businessman, politician and the designer of a more comfortable bicycle seat, built this combination of Richardsonian Romanesque and Shingle styles mansion. The outstanding interior features include intricately carved woodwork, a grand staircase, Tiffany windows and a Gothic chapel. The home reflects the opulent era at the turn of the century. Displays are shown throughout the house including a garment collection in the third floor ballroom. Also, there is a local history library.
NRHP
Lorain County Historical Society

FAIRPORT

FAIRPORT HARBOR LIGHTKEEPER'S HOME & TOWER, 1825; 1871
FAIRPORT MARINE MUSEUM
129 Second Street
Fairport Harbor, Ohio 44077
Lake County
(216) 354-4825

**Fourth Sat of May through
second Sun of September
Sat, Sun, Wed, and holidays/1-6
Group tours during off-hours
by appointment**

Admission fee

Designed by architect, Jonathan Goldsmith, the lightkeeper's home and lighthouse
were originally built in 1825 and subsequently rebuilt in 1871. Now these structures
house the artifacts of the Fairport Marine Museum. In the conical tower, a 69-step
spiral staircase leads to the observation platform from where Lake Erie and Grand
River can be viewed. This beacon of light aided Lake Erie navigators until 1925; it
also guided runaway slaves along the Underground Railroad. An equipped pilot house
from the Great Lakes freighter "Frontenac" is attached to the lightkeeper's home.
Numerous exhibits pertaining to Great Lakes navigation and early local history are on
display.
NRHP
Fairport Harbor Historical Society

FINDLAY

HULL HOUSE, mid 1800's
422 West Sandusky Street
Findlay, Ohio 45840
Hancock County
(419) 423-4433

Open year around Th, Fri, Sun/1-4

The Italianate Victorian red brick house, with a modified mansard roof and overhang-
ing eaves, was built by Jasper Hull, local banker and gas light entrepreneur. A few
photographs and family items are on display. A second owner, Harry Flater, built the
large Colonial Revival style front porch onto the house. The museum presents several special exhibitions on topics relating to the history of Hancock County. A collection of late nineteenth century pressed glass made in Findlay is on permanent display.
NRHP
Hancock Historical Museum Association

FRANKLIN

GENERAL FORREST HARDING MEMORIAL MUSEUM, 1901
302 Park Avenue
Franklin, Ohio 45005
Warren County
(513) 746-8295 or (513) 746-4466

April-November/Sun/2-5
Tours by appointment

Admission fee

This beautiful, large late Victorian frame dwelling, considered as home by Harding during all of his years of military service, was built by his parents, Clarence and Lilly Harding. Major General Forrest E. Harding was a West Point graduate who served in both the first and second World Wars. He made a name for himself when he refused General MacArthur's order to attack Buna in the Pacific in 1942 because his men were ill-equipped and suffering from widespread sickness. Although removed from his command, he was later vindicated for his decision. After retirement, he was instrumental in establishing the Franklin Area Historical Society and left his home and most of the furnishings for its use. Each room downstairs is of a different wood: the Center Room—quarter-sawed oak; Northeast Parlor—cherry; Library—mahogany; Dining Room—curly birch. The oriental rugs, the sliding "pocket doors" and the stained glass windows are worthy of note.
Franklin Area Historical Society

FREMONT

DILLON HOUSE, 1873
1329 Buckland Avenue
Fremont, Ohio 43420
Sandusky County
(419) 332-2081

By appointment only

Admission fee

Architect John C. Johnson built this Second Empire house for Charles M. Dillon, founder of the Fremond Grund Drug Company, and it was occupied by the family until 1960. Mrs. Ann Dillon was the daughter of Ralph P. Buckland, the first law partner of President Hayes. In 1962 the Hayes Foundation purchased the home and has now restored it to its original grandeur. Noteworthy are its wall decorations, wood shutters, door frames and stairwell. Fine period furnishings and appropriate decor add to its charm. The house serves as a guest house and is available for meetings and social functions.
Rutherford B. Hayes Presidential Center
Photo courtesy of the Rutherford B. Hayes Presidential Center

RUTHERFORD B. HAYES PRESIDENTIAL CENTER, 1859-1863; additions

Spiegel Grove
1337 Hayes Ave.
Fremont, Ohio 43420
Sandusky County
(419) 332-2081

January-December/Mon-Sat/9-5
Sun & holidays/Noon-5
Call for dates and times
for Christmas tours

Admission fee, Library no charge

Behind iron gates that once guarded the White House stands Spiegel Grove, the 25 acre wooded estate inherited by Rutherford B. Hayes from his uncle, Sardis Birchard. The 19th century Victorian style mansion was built as a summer home by Birchard and it became the home of the future 19th President of the U.S. in 1873. Original family portraits and fine furnishings remain in the spacious house, which has had additions. The private and public family possessions and mementos on view offer a unique glimpse into the America of 100 years ago. In December the house is beautifully decorated for a grand Victorian Christmas. The site includes the tombs of President and Mrs. Hayes and a memorial building housing a museum and library. The Hayes Library was the first presidential library and serves as a renowned American historical research center.

NRHP-NHL
Ohio Historical Society
Rutherford B. Hayes Presidential Center
Photo courtesy of the Rutherford B. Hayes Presidential Center

GALLIPOLIS

OUR HOUSE MUSEUM, 1819

432 First Avenue
Gallipolis, Ohio 45631
Gallia County
(614) 446-0596

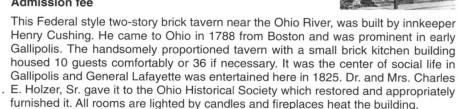

Memorial Day-Labor Day/Tues-Sat/10-5/Sun/1-5
May, September, October/Sat & Sun/1-5

Admission fee

This Federal style two-story brick tavern near the Ohio River, was built by innkeeper Henry Cushing. He came to Ohio in 1788 from Boston and was prominent in early Gallipolis. The handsomely proportioned tavern with a small brick kitchen building housed 10 guests comfortably or 36 if necessary. It was the center of social life in Gallipolis and General Lafayette was entertained here in 1825. Dr. and Mrs. Charles
. E. Holzer, Sr. gave it to the Ohio Historical Society which restored and appropriately furnished it. All rooms are lighted by candles and fireplaces heat the building.
NRHP
Ohio Historical Society - OHS Photo

GENEVA

JENNIE MUNGER GREGORY MEMORIAL MUSEUM, 1823-26; addition
Between Putnam and Grandview Drives
Geneva-on-the-Lake, Ohio 44041
Ashtabula County
(216) 466-7337

Memorial Day-Labor Day/Wed and Sat/10-4

Donation

Solomon Fitch, a pioneer from New England, purchased this lake-front property in 1818, and his son, Thomas, built the first frame house in the area on the Lake Erie shore. The Christian doors which represent the cross and open Bible and huge supporting beams are interesting features. In front of the house, the pier for dockage for the Fitch and Spencer lumber shipping business was known as "Fitch's Landing". The house was willed to the Society by Jennie Munger Gregory. It now serves as a museum with period rooms.
Ashtabula County Historical Society

Shandy Hall

SHANDY HALL, 1815; additions
6333 South Ridge West
Geneva, Ohio 44041
Ashtabula County
(216) 466-3680

May-October/Tu-Sat/10-5/Sun and holidays/1-5

Admission fee

One of the oldest houses remaining in the Western Reserve, this is a saltbox style frame house, built by Colonel Robert Harper, son of a Connecticut pioneer and land speculator, who came to the Western Reserve in 1798. Much of the interior could be described as elegant country style. Many of the 19th century antique furnishings belonged to and reflect the life style of the Harper family. A rare block-printed French wallpaper (c. 1815) decorates the coved ceiling dining room. Empire furniture, wallpaper and damask curtains are in the parlor. The remaining rooms are appropriately furnished including the cellar kitchen.
NRHP
Western Reserve Historical Society

GEORGETOWN

ULYSSES S. GRANT BOYHOOD HOME, 1823-1824; 1828

219 E. Grant Avenue
Entry Thompson House Gallery
203 E. Grant Avenue
Georgetown, Ohio 45121
Brown County
(513) 378-4222

January-December
Mon-Thurs/9-1/Sat/2-5
or by appointment

The earliest part of the simple two-story brick Federal style house was built by Jesse R. Grant, Ulysses S. Grant's father. As his family grew, and his business prospered, Jesse built a three-room addition. Ulysses S. Grant served as General-in-Chief of Armies and was the eighteenth President of the United States. He lived in the house from 1823-1839, at which time he entered West Point. The house contains some Grant furnishings and artifacts.
NRHP-NHL
Privately owned

GRANVILLE

GRANVILLE LIFESTYLE MUSEUM, 1870-1871

H.D. ROBINSON HOUSE

121 S. Main Street
Granville, Ohio 43023
Licking County
(614) 587-0373

Mid-April to mid-October/Sun/1-4:30
Other days group tours by appointment
Christmas Open House: first Sunday in December (No charge)

Admission fee

A spacious front porch, a later addition to the Robinson's Italianate house, welcomes visitors with a sign, "Hubert's porch—sit and relax." The sign reflects the atmosphere of the Robinsons' home. Hubert and Oese Robinson lived in the house from 1917 until their deaths, Hubert in 1960, Oese in 1981. Visitors tour nine rooms featuring unique exhibits of family possessions dating back to Hubert's step-great grandfather, Martin Root. Mr. Root drove a wagon with the first settlers to Granville, Ohio, from Granville, Massachusetts in 1805. Furnishings are mostly late Victorian. Group tours include a choice of programs with narrator and models: Victorian Undergarments or Victorian Flirts, and Oese's garden, in season.
NRHP
Hubert and Oese Robinson Foundation

ROBBINS HUNTER MUSEUM 1842; additions
(AVERY-DOWNER HOUSE)
221 East Broadway
Granville, Ohio 43023
Licking County
(614) 587-0430

April-September/Tu-Sun/1-5
October-December/Fri-Sun/1-5

Donations/fee for group tours

Built for Alfred Avery from designs by architect Minard LaFever, this stately house is an outstanding example of Greek Revival architecture. It follows the line and detailing of a classical Greek temple with the central portico supported by fluted Ionic columns and the symmetrical side wings by Doric columns. The House contains some original furnishings. Robbins Hunter, Jr., the last owner, filled the house with period antiques and memorabilia. An historian and collector of note, Mr. Hunter bequeathed this house and contents to the Licking County Historical Society in 1979.
NRHP
Licking County Historical Society

GREENVILLE

GARST MUSEUM, 1852; additions
205 North Broadway
Greenville, Ohio 45331
Darke County
(513) 548-5250

February-December/Tu-Sun/1-4:30

Donation

Lowell Thomas' Birthplace House

This two-story Federal vernacular brick building was built by George Coover as an inn for travelers along the Dayton and Union Railroad which ran beside the house. The Garst family owned the building from 1861 to 1946 when they gave it to the Darke County Historical Society to operate as an historical museum. Among the large variety of exhibits are Indian relics, old kitchen equipment and much early Americana. One wing includes mementos of two of Darke County's famous natives, Lowell Thomas and Annie Oakley. Another addition houses collections and artifacts which demonstrate 19th century America. In 1987 *Lowell Thomas' Birthplace House* was moved from Woodington, Ohio, to the grounds of the museum. It has been completely restored and furnished in the period of 1892, the year of Thomas' birth.
NRHP
Darke County Historical Society

HAMILTON

BENNINGHOFEN HOUSE, 1861

327 North Second Street
Hamilton, Ohio 45011
Butler County
(513) 893-7111

January-December
Tu-Sun/1-4/Closed holidays
Groups by appointment only

Admission fee

This fine Italian Villa style house was the home of a prominent Miami Valley industrialist, financier and philanthropist, John Benninghofen, who purchased it in 1874. Located in the German Village district, the house has been refurbished and is well furnished in the late Victorian style. A Victorian iron fence encloses the grounds. It contains historical documents, antique jewelry and other collections of historical interest. The house was given as a gift in 1947 to the Butler County Historical Society by Miss Pauline Benninghofen.
NRHP
Butler County Historical Society

CRAWFORD HOUSE, 1835

2200 Hancock Avenue
Hamilton, Ohio 45011
Butler County
(513) 867-5835

January-December/Mon-Fri/8:30-5

The Crawford House, an early brick farm house, was built on sixty-five acres of land owned by David Crawford, a member of a Revolutionary War family. The ten-room house has tulip, popular and walnut woodwork, oak and ash floors and a shake shingle roof. The stone foundations were made of native fieldstone. Its bricks were made from blue clay hand-molded and kilned on the grounds. The home and grounds were donated to the City of Hamilton in 1967. The home was leased to and restored by the Butler County Park District. It now houses the Administrative Office, a natural history library, a museum room and a meeting room available for public use.
Metro Parks of Butler County

LANE-HOOVEN HOUSE, 1863; addition

319 North Third Street
Hamilton, Ohio 45011
Butler County
(513) 863-1389

January-December/Mon-Fri/9-5

This Victorian Gothic style two-story brick dwelling was built in the octagon mode by Clark Lane, a prosperous steam engine manufacturer. The house has eclectic architectural features typical of the period, such as the Tudor front doors, gothic arched windows, and the cast iron tracery of the balconies. A circular stairway extends to the octagonal tower. The four bedrooms have arched doors and vaulted ceilings. The house has undergone a 1978 restoration. The Hamilton Community Foundation has offices here. The octagonal Tuscany Revival Style library (1866) across the street was also built, furnished and donated to the city by Lane.
NRHP
Hamilton Community Foundation
Photo by Patrick Brown

PIONEER LOG CABIN, c. 1804

Monument Park
Corner of High and Monument Avenue
Hamilton, Ohio 45011
Butler County
(513) 867-5835

January-December/Wed-Sun/9-4

This one-room hewn log house with a loft was built before 1804. Formerly located in Rossville, it has had fifty-seven owners. In 1964 it was purchased by a realtor who planned to raze it to make room for a parking lot. When its exterior clapboard siding was removed and its logs revealed, it was donated to the Butler County Park District. The house was then moved and reconstructed.
Metro Parks of Butler County

HARRISON

GOVERNOR OTHNIEL LOOKER HOME, 1804-1805

10580 Marvin Road
Harrison, Ohio 45030
Hamilton County
(513) 367-4984

May-October
Third Sun of month/1:30-4

This Federal vernacular style frame house was built by New Jersey native Othniel Looker and his sons shortly after their arrival in Ohio. Looker served in the Revolutionary War under General George Washington. An early member of the Ohio Legislature, he became Governor of Ohio in 1814.
NRHP
Village Historical Society, Inc.

HILLSBORO

HIGHLAND HOUSE, 1842-1844; late 19th century addition

151 East Main Street
Hillsboro, Ohio 45133
Highland County
(513) 393-3392

March-December/Fri/1-5/Sun/1-4

Donation

This eighteen-room Federal style brick house was built for the Peter L. Ayres family. Later it became an inn and was used for that purpose until early in the 20th century when it was converted into a rooming house. In 1965, the Highland County Historical Society acquired Highland House. It is now a museum house which is furnished with some pieces dating back to the 1700's.
NRHP
Highland County Historical Society

HIRAM

JOHN JOHNSON HISTORIC FARM HOME, 1829-1830

6203 Pioneer Trail
Hiram, Ohio 44234
Portage County
(216) 569-3170

Open year round except Thanksgiving and Christmas/9-Dusk

The house remains much as it was when it was built by John Johnson who had come from Vermont in 1818. There were several owners before the house was purchased by the Mormon Church (The Church of Jesus Christ of Latter-Day Saints) in 1956. The keep has the original mantle and fireplace with the original cooking arm. The old oven, where as many as eighteen loaves of bread were baked at one time, also remains. There is a summer kitchen, dining/conference room and the bedroom from which Mormon leader, Joseph Smith was taken to be tarred and feathered in 1832. The Church purchased the house because Joseph Smith lived in it in 1831-1832.
The Church of the Latter Day Saints

HUDSON

FREDERICK BALDWIN HOUSE, 1834; additions

22 Aurora Street
Hudson, Ohio 44236
Summit County
(216) 653-6658

January-December/Mon, Th/9-9
Fri, Sat/9-5/Sun/Noon-5

Built by Frederick Baldwin, this Greek Revival house has retained much of its original appearance. Frederick's daughter, Caroline, was born here. She founded the Hudson Library and Historical Society which bought the house in 1922. The house was opened as a public library in 1925 with funds from her will. Restorations and additions have been made. The building is a functioning part of the library. One room, the Simon Reading Room, is available for public use. It contains a 19th century art collection as well as other artifacts. An extensive research collection on Hudson and on abolitionist John Brown is available in another area of the library. The house is in the Hudson Historic District.
NRHP
Hudson Library and Historical Society

LAKEWOOD

OLDEST STONE HOUSE, 1838
14710 Lake Avenue, Lakewood Park
Lakewood, Ohio 44107
Cuyahoga County
(216) 221-7343

February-November/Wed/1-4/Sun/2-5
Closed national holidays

This Greek Revival stone dwelling was built beside the Detroit Road, a main thoroughfare. It has been moved, restored and furnished in the early 19th century period. The kitchen, parlor, birthing room and two bedrooms contain furniture and accessories. Demonstrations include quilting, cooking in the fireplace and periodic special displays. An extensive herb garden is laid out behind the house.
NRHP
Lakewood Historical Society

LANCASTER

THE GEORGIAN, 1832
105 East Wheeling Street
Lancaster, Ohio 43130
Fairfield County
(614) 654-9923

April-December/Tu-Sun/1-4
last tour 3:15 or by appointment
closed holidays

This handsome brick home was built for Samuel MacCracken, an influential business man who came from Pennsylvania in 1810. He engaged Daniel Sifford, a respected local builder, to construct a house representing the best of American and Georgian architecture. Using Asher Benjamin's *Handbook for Carpenters,* Sifford began the nearly three year project. Although basically Federal in style, the house has Regency features. Each of the five fluted columns on the massive west portico encompass a complete tree trunk for support. Fine furnishings of the 1830's period include some Fairfield County pieces. Located in an historic district, The Georgian is available for meetings and social functions.
NRHP
Fairfield Heritage Association, Inc.

REESE-PETERS HOUSE, 1834

145 East Main Street
Lancaster, Ohio 43130
Fairfield County
(614) 687-7190

House restoration is on-going.
Call ahead for status and hours of operation.

William J. Reese was born and educated in Philadelphia. In 1827, he came to Lancaster to practice law. He was a brilliant young man and soon became one of Lancaster's most prominent citizens. In 1829 he married Mary Elizabeth Sherman, sister of William Tecumseh Sherman, and they built this fine house. The interior workmanship is significant. The woodwork is thought to have been hand carved in Philadelphia by a pupil of William Savery and brought over the mountains in covered wagons to be installed in the house. The unusual rectangular medallion in the entry hall is worthy of note. The Reese-Peters House is considered one of the most refined examples of Transitional Federal Greek Revival architecture. It was a Peters family residence until 1995 when it was given by them to Fairfield County for renovation as a public arts education/decorative arts museum facility. Renovations will be accomplished through the State Capital Improvements Fund administered through the Ohio Arts Facilities Commission.
NRHP
Fairfield County Commissioners

SHERMAN HOUSE, c.1811; additions

137 East Main Street
Lancaster, Ohio 43130
Fairfield County
(614) 687-5891

April-December/Tues-Sun/1-4
Closed holidays
or by appointment

Admission fee

Mr. and Mrs. Charles R. Sherman, parents of two famous Ohioans, General William Tecumseh Sherman and politician John Sherman, occupied this small frame house in 1811. It was expanded in 1816 to better accommodate their family of eleven children. Restored, the house contains Sherman family memorabilia, period rooms, and a re-creation of General Sherman's field tent. The 1869 Italianate addition houses Civil War exhibits.
NRHP-NHL
Fairfield Heritage Association

LEBANON

GLENDOWER, 1836; additions
Orchard Avenue
Lebanon, Ohio 45036
Warren County
(513) 932-5366

**Memorial Day-Labor Day/Wed-Sat/10-4
Sun/1-4**

Admission fee

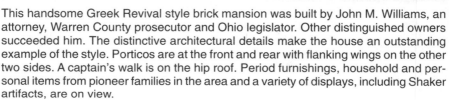

This handsome Greek Revival style brick mansion was built by John M. Williams, an attorney, Warren County prosecutor and Ohio legislator. Other distinguished owners succeeded him. The distinctive architectural details make the house an outstanding example of the style. Porticos are at the front and rear with flanking wings on the other two sides. A captain's walk is on the hip roof. Period furnishings, household and personal items from pioneer families in the area and a variety of displays, including Shaker artifacts, are on view.
NRHP
Ohio Historical Society - OHS Photo
Warren County Historical Society Museum
Warren County Convention and Visitors Bureau

LIMA

THE MacDONELL HOUSE 1893; 1897
632 West Market Street
Lima, Ohio 45801
Allen County
(419) 224-1113

**Sept-May/Tu-Sun/1-5
June-August/Tu-Sat/10-5/Sun/1-5
Closed holidays**

This stately Victorian Shingle style house appears today much as it did when built by Frank Banta a candy and chewing gum manufacturer. A rear addition, built by John VanDyke, a Standard Oil executive, expanded the home to its current 28 rooms. The house is evocative of life in Lima as the town prospered after the discovery of oil in 1885. The furnishings are Victorian. The hand-carved oak, cherry and mahogany woodwork is noteworthy. There are six gas fireplaces, chandeliers and a beautiful 20-pane stained glass window on the stair landing. Six bathrooms are also included in the home, some with marble floors and walls. The last owners, Mr. and Mrs. J.A. MacDonell, decorated the home to reflect the elaborate style of the 1890's, and donated it to the Allen County Historical Society. On the adjacent property is a furnished log house representing the earlier, simpler life of the 1840's.
NRHP
Allen County Historical Society

LONDON

JONATHAN ALDER CABIN, 1806
c/o Madison County Historical Society
260 East High Street
London, Ohio 43140
Madison County
(614) 852-2977

**First Sat and Sun/1-4/Wed/1-4
or by appointment**

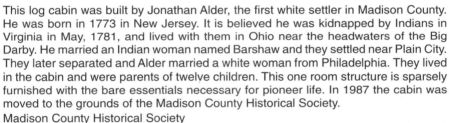

This log cabin was built by Jonathan Alder, the first white settler in Madison County. He was born in 1773 in New Jersey. It is believed he was kidnapped by Indians in Virginia in May, 1781, and lived with them in Ohio near the headwaters of the Big Darby. He married an Indian woman named Barshaw and they settled near Plain City. They later separated and Alder married a white woman from Philadelphia. They lived in the cabin and were parents of twelve children. This one room structure is sparsely furnished with the bare essentials necessary for pioneer life. In 1987 the cabin was moved to the grounds of the Madison County Historical Society.
Madison County Historical Society

LOVELAND

RICH LOG CABIN, 1797
c/o Greater Loveland Historical Society Museum
201 Riverside Drive
Loveland, Ohio 45140
Hamilton County
(513) 683-5692

Fri,Sat, Sun/1-4:30 and by appointment

This log cabin is one of the oldest structures in the greater Loveland area. It was built by Thomas B. Rich and his wife Mary Ann (Barry) Rich. Located on a land grant given to Thomas' grandfather as payment for his services as a Revolutionary War Captain, the site offered a natural spring and was close to the Little Miami River. The cabin was constructed of hand hewn native oak, walnut and hickory logs atop a limestone foundation with walls two feet thick. During the mid-1800's a room was added to the rear of the cabin. In the 1890's the roof line was raised to accommodate a loft for the family of eleven children and a two room addition was constructed. The entire structure was covered with stucco in the early 1900's. The Log Cabin was donated to The Greater Loveland Historical Society Museum by Kris and Angie Hawk. It was dismantled and moved to the museum site in late 1994. Restoration is to be complete in 1996.
Greater Loveland Historical Society Museum

LUCAS

MALABAR FARM STATE PARK- MALABAR FARM HOUSE, 1830
BROMFIELD ADDITION, 1939
Box 4050 Bromfield Road
4 miles SW of Lucas
Lucas, Ohio 44843
Richland County
(419) 892-2784

January-December/Mon-Sun/1-5

Admission fee

The original 12 room home was built by Clement Henry. Louis Bromfield, author and Pulitzer Prize winner, supervised the design and construction of the "Big House". Bromfield kept four rooms of the old farmhouse and added 28 more to comprise the sprawling white clapboard Western Reserve style farmhouse that remains today. The house has a two story center section and wings encompassing 32 rooms and a spacious veranda overlooking the garden. Of special interest is the hanging double staircase. The furnishings remain as they were at the time of Bromfield's death. They include 17th and 18th century French provincial furniture from his villa in France, his desk and books. Lauren Bacall and Humphrey Bogart married and honeymooned here. The nearby Malabar Inn (1820) is listed under Perrysville but is actually part of Malabar State Park.
NRHP
Malabar Farm State Park

MANSFIELD

THE BUSHNELL HOUSE, 1893
The Ohio Genealogical Society
34 Sturges Ave
P.O. Box 2625
Mansfield, Ohio 44906-0625
Richland County
(419) 522-9077

Year round/Tu-Sat/9-5
Fee for use of genealogy library

The 27-room Bushnell House was constructed in the Richardsonian Romanesque style by Martin Baldwin Bushnell (1837-1923), a Mansfield banker, park commissioner, Mansfield City Schools director, and president of the North American Watch Company. The exterior features an octagonal tower, turret, stone pillars in the middle of windows, and an immediate sense of massiveness from the locally quarried red

continued

sandstone blocks. The interior, largely remodeled, still features several ornate fireplaces, a lovely stained glass window, and handsomely carved woodwork of sycamore, oak, and maple. Since 1987, the Bushnell House has served as headquarters and library for the 6500 member Ohio Genealogical Society, a non-profit organization dedicated to preserving the history of Ohio families.
NRHP
The Ohio Genealogical Society, Inc.

KINGWOOD HALL, 1926
900 Park Avenue, West
Mansfield, Ohio 44906
Richland County
(419) 522-0211

January-December/Tu-Sat/9-5
April-October/Sun/1:30-4:30

This French Renaissance Revival mansion was built by Charles K. King chairman of the board of Ohio Brass Company. It was designed by Clarence Mack after a French chateau in Normandy. Many of the original furnishings are on view. King left the estate to be used as a horticulture center for the general public. A library and meeting place are available. The gardens on the 47 acre estate are renowned.
NRHP
Kingwood Center

OAK HILL COTTAGE, 1847
310 Springmill Street
Mansfield, Ohio 44902
Richland County
(419) 524-1765

April-December/Sun/2-5
Closed Christmas Day
Group tours can be arranged by phone.

Oak Hill Cottage is one of the finest Gothic houses in the United States. It has seven gables, five double chimneys and seven marble fireplaces. The original furnishings and family artifacts have been preserved. Louis Bromfield, a native of Mansfield and Pulitzer Prize winning author, played at Oak Hill as a child. His memories of the home were the basis for *Shane's Castle* in his 1924 novel *The Green Bay Tree.*
NRHP
Richland County
Richland County Historical Society

MARIETTA

CAMPUS MARTIUS/OHIO RIVER MUSEUM
601 Second Street
Marietta, Ohio 45750
Washington County
(614) 373-3750

May-September/Mon-Sat/9:30-5
March-April, October-November
Wed-Sat/9:30-5
Sun/Noon-5/Closed holidays

Admission fee

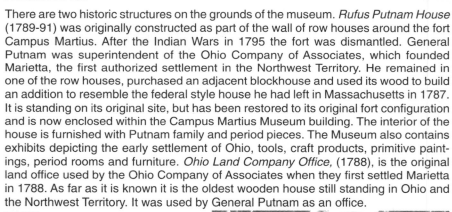

There are two historic structures on the grounds of the museum. *Rufus Putnam House* (1789-91) was originally constructed as part of the wall of row houses around the fort Campus Martius. After the Indian Wars in 1795 the fort was dismantled. General Putnam was superintendent of the Ohio Company of Associates, which founded Marietta, the first authorized settlement in the Northwest Territory. He remained in one of the row houses, purchased an adjacent blockhouse and used its wood to build an addition to resemble the federal style house he had left in Massachusetts in 1787. It is standing on its original site, but has been restored to its original fort configuration and is now enclosed within the Campus Martius Museum building. The interior of the house is furnished with Putnam family and period pieces. The Museum also contains exhibits depicting the early settlement of Ohio, tools, craft products, primitive paintings, period rooms and furniture. *Ohio Land Company Office,* (1788), is the original land office used by the Ohio Company of Associates when they first settled Marietta in 1788. As far as it is known it is the oldest wooden house still standing in Ohio and the Northwest Territory. It was used by General Putnam as an office.
NRHP
Ohio Historical Society

THE CASTLE c.1855
418 Fourth Street
Marietta, Ohio 45750
Washington County
(614) 373-4180

April 15-October/Th-Mon/November 1-April 14/Fri-Mon
Weekdays 10-4/Sat, Sun/1-4/closed New Year's Day, Easter, Thanksgiving, Christmas

The Castle, located in the heart of Marietta's historic district, is an outstanding example of Gothic Revival architecture with its arched doorways, trefoil attic windows, and the octagonal tower which is its focal point. The tower rises 70 feet above the ground and in winter both the Muskingum and Ohio Rivers can be seen from the top. Stepping though the iron gates a visitor gets a feel of the gracious lifestyle of 19th century Marietta. The home features an impressive front parlor with its original chandelier, scagliola mantel, and interior oak shutters which close over the ceiling to

continued

floor bay window. Fine craftsmanship is to be found throughout the house and the charming adjacent carriage house. The house is partially furnished with pieces of historical significance to the area. It also features changing exhibits of art and history important to the region.
Betsey Mills Corporation

HENRY FEARING HOUSE, 1847; additions 1870

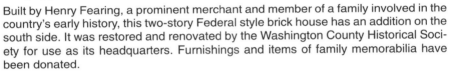

131 Gilman Street
Marietta, Ohio 45750
Washington County
(614) 373-3226

**April-October/Sat-Sun/1-5
or by appointment**

Built by Henry Fearing, a prominent merchant and member of a family involved in the country's early history, this two-story Federal style brick house has an addition on the south side. It was restored and renovated by the Washington County Historical Society for use as its headquarters. Furnishings and items of family memorabilia have been donated.
NRHP
Washington County Historical Society

MARION

WARREN G. HARDING HOME, 1891

380 Mt. Vernon Avenue
Marion, Ohio 43302
Marion County
(614) 387-9630

**Memorial Day-Labor Day/Wed-Sat/9:30-5
Sun/Noon-5
Weekends in September and October**

Admission fee

Warren G. Harding, publisher of *The Marion Star,* built this Victorian style house for his "Duchess", Florence Kling DeWolfe. Married in the reception hall, they resided in the home until leaving for the White House in 1921. Here he conducted his "Front Porch Campaign" of 1920. The house has been restored and contains original furnishings. The press corps building in back of the home is the President Harding Museum.
NRHP-NHL
OHS photo

HENRY TRUE HOME, 1848

139 East Church Street
Marion, Ohio 43302
Marion County
(614) 387-7150 or (614) 387-6140

Daily by appointment

This Gothic Revival style house was
the home of Henry A. True, grandson
of Ozias Bowen, who built what is now
the Stengel-True Museum. Preservation of historic houses and their furnish-
ings interested him, consequently he willed his house to be used as a museum. The
Victorian period contents of his home are as he had them and reflect the time when
the house was built.
NRHP
Marion Historical Association
The Stengel-True Museum, Inc.

STENGEL-TRUE MUSEUM, 1864

504 South State Street, at Washington Street
Marion, Ohio 43302
Marion County
(614) 387-7150

Sat-Sun/1-4:30

This fine Italianate style house was designed and built by Ozias Bowen, Judge of the
Ohio Supreme Court. Each room contains a coal burning fireplace with marble mantles
and fronts. The lifetime collections of Americana belonging to Dr. Frederick A. Stengel,
optometrist and jeweler, are displayed throughout the house. Lighting devices, music
boxes, guns, clocks and glass are among the many artifacts exhibited. A view of
Marion can be seen from the cupola. Bowen's grandson, Henry A. True, made it
possible to have the house preserved as a museum.
NRHP
Marion-Historical Association
The Stengel-True Museum, Inc.

MARTINS FERRY

SEDGWICK HOUSE MUSEUM, 1872
627 Hanover Street
Martins Ferry, Ohio 43935
Balmont County
(614) 635-4222

**May-October/Tu-Sat/Noon-4
or by appointment**

Admission fee

The house was built by Henry Helling, President of Northwood Glass Company, as a wedding gift for his son, Charles, secretary of Northwood Glass. The Leroy Sedgwick family later owned the house. There is an extensive collection of Ohio Valley glass, vintage dresses from 1840's to 1900's, quilts and linens. Rooms contain memorabilia and artifacts of early history of Martins Ferry and the area.
Martins Ferry Area Historical Society, Inc.
Photo courtesy of Martins Ferry Area Historical Society, Inc.

MASSILLON

FIVE OAKS, 1892-1894
210 Fourth Street, N.E.
Massillon, Ohio 44646
Stark County
(216) 833-4896

**July-August/Th, Sat, Sun/1-4
or by appointment for groups of 15 or more**

Admission fee

Designed by noted Cleveland architect, Charles F. Schweinfurth, this palatial Romanesque Revival mansion was built by Mr. J. Walter McClymonds, an industrialist and banker. The ornately carved woodwork, large marble fireplaces, Louis Tiffany window and glass lighting fixtures, furnishings and third floor ballroom all add to the opulence of the house. A luncheon arrangement may be made with a group tour September-June.
NRHP
Massillon Heritage Foundation, Inc.

SPRING HILL HISTORIC HOME, 1821-1824

1244 Wales Road N.E.
Massillon, Ohio 44646
Stark County
(216) 833-6749

June-August/Wed, Th, Sun/1-4
April, May, September, October
by appointment only

Admission fee

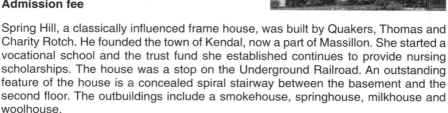

Spring Hill, a classically influenced frame house, was built by Quakers, Thomas and Charity Rotch. He founded the town of Kendal, now a part of Massillon. She started a vocational school and the trust fund she established continues to provide nursing scholarships. The house was a stop on the Underground Railroad. An outstanding feature of the house is a concealed spiral stairway between the basement and the second floor. The outbuildings include a smokehouse, springhouse, milkhouse and woolhouse.
NRHP
Massillon Museum Foundation, Inc.

MAUMEE

WOLCOTT HOUSE MUSEUM COMPLEX, c. 1836

1031 River Road
Maumee, Ohio 43537
Lucas County
(419) 893-9602

April-December/Wed-Sun/1-4
or by appointment

Admission fee

Maumee was a frontier village when James and Mary Wolcott, the granddaughter of the Miami Indian Chief Little Turtle, arrived in 1826. Soon after, they built their large Federal vernacular style clapboard home with its two-story veranda overlooking the Maumee River and Wolcott's steamship landing. Wolcott became both a Lucas County judge and mayor of Maumee. The interior is filled with family pieces and furnishings appropriate for a mid-19th century community leader. Some rooms are used as exhibit areas displaying Indian artifacts, quilts, china, toys, clothing and items of local history. The *Wolcott Historic Complex* includes a furnished 1841 Greek Revival saltbox farmhouse; an 1850 log cabin; an 1880 depot and caboose; and a 1901 country church, all authentically furnished. An 1841 Greek Revival townhouse houses the Talking Turtle Gift Shop.
NRHP
Maumee Valley Historical Society

MENTOR

LAWNFIELD, c.1830; additions
JAMES A. GARFIELD NATIONAL HISTORIC SITE
8095 Mentor Avenue
Mentor, Ohio 44060
Lake County
(216) 255-8722

Home closed for renovation until at least 1997.
Call ahead for status.
Visitors Center scheduled to open summer of 1996

The large Victorian frame house was the home of President James A. Garfield. It contains Garfield family furnishings, possessions and memorabilia. The barn on the property has been restored and now is the visitors center. The center will include a gift shop, an audio-visual on James A. Garfield and exhibits interpreting the life of Garfield. The north end of the property will also be available for visitors to stroll around. There will be four wayside exhibits in place describing the 1880 farm, the carriage house, the railroad connection and the only barn remaining from Garfield's lifetime.
NRHP-NHL
The National Park Service
Western Reserve Historical Society

MILAN

THOMAS ALVA EDISON BIRTHPLACE MUSEUM, 1842
9 Edison Drive, Box 451
Milan, Ohio 44846
Erie County
(419) 499-2135

January by appointment
February-May/Tu-Sun/1-5
June 1-Labor Day/Tu-Sat/10-5/Sun/1-5
Labor Day-November 30/Tu-Sun/1-5
Closed Thanksgiving and December
Last tour 4:30 - 45 minutes in duration

Admission fee

This two-story Greek Revival vernacular style brick house in which the inventor was born in 1847 and where he spent his first seven years was built by his father, Samuel Edison. Thomas Edison owned it from 1906 to 1931. His wife and daughter restored it. The furnishings belonged to different family members who resided in the home. There are exhibits of family mementos including letters, photographs and models of the original phonograph and incandescent light. Filled with period articles used in daily living, the basement kitchen overlooks the Milan Canal Basin.
NRHP-NHL
Edison Birthplace Association, Inc.

MILAN HISTORICAL MUSEUM

10 Edison Drive
Milan, Ohio 44846
Erie County
(419) 499-2968

April, May, September, October/Tu-Sun/1-5
June, July, August/Tu-Sat/10-5/Sun/1-5
Donation

The *Dr. Lehman Galpin House* (c. 1846), a handsome Greek Revival brick house, was built by Dr. Galpin who assisted at the birth of Thomas A. Edison. The parlor is furnished with antiques. Other rooms house exhibits including an outstanding collection of glass, antique dolls, guns and Americana of all kinds. *The Sayles House* (1843), a frame house in the Western Reserve style, was last lived in by Robert C. Sayles and its restoration was made possible through his estate. The house contains 19th century furniture and a weaving room with early Pennsylvania and Ohio spinning, flax and wool wheels. There is an 1850 rosewood melodeon in the parlor. The Milan Historical Museum complex includes a country store, blacksmith shop and Memorial Arts building.
Milan Historical Museum, Inc.

MILFORD

PROMONT, 1867
906 Main Street
Milford, Ohio 45150
Clermont County
(513) 248-0324

Fri and Sun/1:30-4:30
Special tours by appointment

Admission fee

Promont is an Italianate style house with unique architectural elements. It was called the finest house in Clermont County when built. Promont was the home of Ohio Governor John M. Pattison from 1879-1906. Today the house stands as a living history museum depicting Victorian life. Complete with old toys, Victorian furnishings and clothing, Promont is providing educational opportunities for children and adults to learn about and appreciate the past. This magnificent structure with it's four story tower offers a panoramic view of the town. Promont's newly restored gardens enhance the elegance of this beautiful Victorian home.
Milford Area Historical Society

MILLERSBURG

VICTORIAN HOUSE, 1902
484 North Washington Street
Millersburg, Ohio 44654
Holmes County
(216) 674-3975 or (216) 674-1576

**May-October/Th-Sun/1:30-4:30
or by appointment**

Admission fee

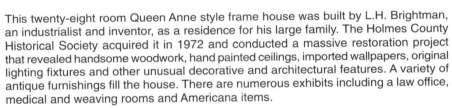

This twenty-eight room Queen Anne style frame house was built by L.H. Brightman, an industrialist and inventor, as a residence for his large family. The Holmes County Historical Society acquired it in 1972 and conducted a massive restoration project that revealed handsome woodwork, hand painted ceilings, imported wallpapers, original lighting fixtures and other unusual decorative and architectural features. A variety of antique furnishings fill the house. There are numerous exhibits including a law office, medical and weaving rooms and Americana items.
NRHP
Holmes County Historical Society

MT. PLEASANT

ELIZABETH HOUSE MANSION MUSEUM, 1835
Union Street
Mt. Pleasant, Ohio 43939
Jefferson County
(614) 769-2893

Open year round by appointment

This handsome brick mansion was built by John Gill who constructed one of the first silk mills in the United States. In 1910 a new owner added a porch with massive columns which were repeated on a smaller scale in the parlor. The house is furnished with period pieces of local historical significance. The house was given to the Mt. Pleasant Historical Society in 1990 by William F. Swabado.
NRHP
Mt. Pleasant Historical Society

QUAKER MEETING HOUSE, 1814

Near S.R. 150
Mt. Pleasant, Ohio 43939
Jefferson County
(614) 769-2893

Open by appointment

Admission fee

This brick Quaker Meeting House, designed by Jacob Ong, architect, is rectangular with a gabled roof, and has separate entrances for men and women and a moveable partition for the seperate sexes. An engineering achievement for its day, the building holds 2000. It was the first Yearly Meeting House for Quaker settlements west of the Allegheny Mountains and the site of anti-slavery activity.
NRHP
Ohio Historical Society
Mt. Pleasant Historical Society

McCONNELSVILLE

EVELYN TRUE BUTTON HOUSE, 1836

142 East Main Street
PO Box 524
McConnelsville, Ohio 43756
Morgan County
(614) 962-4785

**Th, Fri/1-3/Sat/10-Noon
or by appointment**

Donation

This brick and frame house was occupied by Dr. and Mrs. Hiram L. True after their marriage in 1874. Their daughter, Evelyn, was born here. A descendant of General Robert McConnel, founder of McConnelsville, she became an educator, world traveler and author. In 1922 Evelyn True Button and her daughters moved back into her birthplace and she occupied it until her death in 1975. She bequeathed the house and the building next door to the Morgan County Historical Society. The furnishings are of the mid-Victorian period. The Society's office, genealogy room and shops are located in the adjacent building.
NRHP
Morgan County Historical Society

NEW CONCORD

WILLIAM RAINEY HARPER HOUSE, pre-1856

Main Street (U.S. 40)
New Concord, Ohio 43762
Muskingum County
(614) 826-8132

Open by appointment

This two-story log cabin is the birthplace of William R. Harper, a Muskingum College Alumnus who was the first President of the University of Chicago. Built before the Civil War, it includes selected pieces of furniture and Harper memorabilia from the period.
Muskingum College

NEW PHILADELPHIA

SCHOENBRUNN VILLAGE STATE MEMORIAL, 18th century

PO Box 129
East High Avenue
New Philadelphia, Ohio 44663
Tuscarawas County
(216) 339-3636

Memorial Day-Labor Day
Wed-Sat/9:30-5
Sun/Noon-5
September-October/Weekends

Admission fee

Schoenbrunn Village is a reconstruction of Ohio's first Christian settlement, established in 1772 by Moravian Missionaries and their Delaware Indian converts. Seventeen log buildings, including the church and school have been rebuilt. Costumed volunteers demonstrate a variety of pioneer activities.
Ohio Historical Society - OHS photo

NEWARK

DAWESWOOD HOUSE MUSEUM, 1867; addition
7770 Jacksontown Road, S.E.
Newark, Ohio 43056-9380
Licking County
1-800-44-DAWES (443-2937)

**Sat, Sun/3:15 tour
or by appointment**

Admission fee

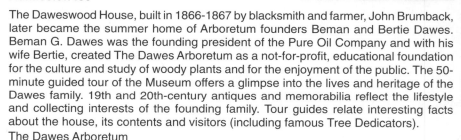

The Daweswood House, built in 1866-1867 by blacksmith and farmer, John Brumback, later became the summer home of Arboretum founders Beman and Bertie Dawes. Beman G. Dawes was the founding president of the Pure Oil Company and with his wife Bertie, created The Dawes Arboretum as a not-for-profit, educational foundation for the culture and study of woody plants and for the enjoyment of the public. The 50-minute guided tour of the Museum offers a glimpse into the lives and heritage of the Dawes family. 19th and 20th-century antiques and memorabilia reflect the lifestyle and collecting interests of the founding family. Tour guides relate interesting facts about the house, its contents and visitors (including famous Tree Dedicators).
The Dawes Arboretum

VETERANS PARK
Sixth and Church Streets
Newark, Ohio 43055
Licking County

Veterans Park which faces Sixth Street
includes three houses
of historical significance:

BUCKINGHAM HOUSE, 1835
(614) 345-6934

Open by appointment/Tu-Fri

A fine example of Greek Revival style, this house was built by Daniel Duncan and later occupied by Judge Jerome Buckingham and his family. Many illustrious guests have visited here including two Presidents of the United States, Rutherford B. Hayes and James A. Garfield; and Civil War Generals Sheridan and Sherman.
Licking County Historical Society

KING HOUSE, 1931
NATIONAL HEISEY GLASS MUSEUM
Sixth and Church Streets
Newark, Ohio 43055
Licking County
(614) 345-2932

January-December/Tu-Sat/10-4/Sun/1-4
Closed holidays

Admission fee

Built in 1831 in the Greek Revival style for prominent attorney Samuel Dennis King, the twice-moved house was originally located on the town square in Newark. It was subsequently occupied by the King family until 1973 when it was slated for demolition. Heisey Collectors of America, Inc. accepted the house as a donation and moved it to its current location to serve as a museum for Heisey glass, made in Newark from 1896-1957. The King House has been renovated twice, including the incorporation of lighted display cabinets. Many of the furnishings, fixtures and memorabilia are from the King family and the original cherry woodwork has been preserved including an arched doorway and hanging staircase. In 1993 the collectors opened an adjacent addition, doubling the size of the glass displays.
Heisey Collectors of America, Inc.

SHERWOOD-DAVIDSON HOUSE, c. 1815
Sixth Street Park
Sixth and West Main Streets
Newark, Ohio 43055
Licking County
(614) 345-4898

March-December/Tu-Sun/tours 1-4
and by appointment
Closed holidays

Admission fee

This museum house is one of the finest examples of Federal Architecture in Ohio. Built by Albert Sherwood, c. 1815, the house is distinguished by its Venetian-arched, two story side gallery and its fan doorway. It was purchased in the 1850's by the Davidson family, three generations of whom resided there. Threatened with demolition in 1947, the house was saved, moved, restored and furnished through the efforts of The Licking County Historical Society. The house is furnished with items from the 1700's and 1800's. Included are a 1740 tall-case clock, a Hepplewhite desk and card table, an early New Hampshire blanket chest, two imposing cherry cupboards and many fine Victorian pieces. The museum also houses outstanding collections of antique toys, dolls and clothing. Accompanying the period rooms is an upstairs gallery where displays are changed on a regular basis.
NRHP
Licking County Historical Society

WEBB HOUSE MUSEUM, 1907
303 Granville Street
Newark, Ohio 43055
Licking County
(614) 345-8540 or (614) 345-4898
April-December/Th, Fri, Sun/1-4

This turn of the century home was given to the Licking County Historical Society by Shirley Pitser Webb. The museum contains family heirlooms and furniture spanning the 19th and early 20th centuries and exhibits from the Society's collections.
NRHP
Licking County Historical Society

NORTH CANTON

HOOVER HISTORICAL CENTER, 1853, 1870
2225 Easton Street N.W.
North Canton, Ohio 44720
Stark County
(216) 499-0287

January-December/Tu-Sun/1-5

Restored in 1978, this Victorian farmhouse, boyhood home of Hoover Company founder, William H. Hoover, the Hoover Historical Center is the only known vacuum cleaner museum in the world. It features an extensive collection of antique and early vacuum cleaners and also memorabilia reflecting growth and development of The Hoover Company and the vacuum cleaner industry. It is owned and completely funded by The Hoover Company of North Canton. Garden tours are available from May through October for six herb gardens which are maintained by Center volunteers. Major exhibit, "Sweeping Changes at East Maple and Main Streets," details technological developments of the vacuum cleaner and its effects on the home and community from 1850 to 1960. Each gallery has a triple focus: a parlor, showing current furniture styling, community activities, and the cleaning methods and vacuums of the particular period being shown.
NRHP
The Hoover Co.

NORTH FAIRFIELD

CHAPMAN HOUSE, c. 1840
7 North Main Street
North Fairfield, Ohio 44855
Huron County
(419) 744-2285

Second Sun in June-last Sun September/1-4

Donation

This small frame house was moved to its present location from a site south of the town in 1841. Its second floor porch with a segmented arch in the gable is unique. Members of the Chapman Family lived here until 1941. The museum was started in 1944 and exhibits items of local interest.
North Fairfield Historical Society

NORWALK

PRESTON-WICKHAM HOUSE, 1835 - FIRELANDS MUSEUM
4 Case Avenue
PO Box 572
Norwalk, Ohio 44857
Huron County
(419) 668-6038

**April, May, September, October, November
Sat and Sun/12-4/June-August
Tu-Sun/12-5/Closed December-March
except by appointment**

This lovely Federal style frame house was built by Samuel Preston, a local newspaper editor, as a wedding gift for his daughter and her husband Frederick Wickham. Until 1860 the newspaper *Reflector Herald* was printed on the second floor. At that time the Wickham family had grown to thirteen members. Now a museum, the house contains antique guns, early lighting devices, local history artifacts and many other items of Americana. The library houses volumes for historical genealogical research.
NRHP
Firelands Historical Society

OBERLIN

OBERLIN HISTORIC SITES
OBERLIN HISTORICAL IMPROVEMENT ORGANIZATION
73 1/2 South Professor Street
PO Box 0455
Oberlin, Ohio 44074
Lorain County
(216) 774-1700

Tu, Wed, Th/tours 1, 2, 3, 4
First Sun, third Sat of each month/1, 2, 3
Closed holidays and week between Christmas
and New Year's Day

Admission fee

James Monroe House

The *James Monroe House* (1866), a brick Italianate-style house, was moved to its present site in 1960. It was originally the home of Civil War General Giles W. Shurtleff, the leader of the first African-American regiment from Ohio to serve in the Civil War. The house was subsequently the long-time home of James Monroe and his wife, Julia Finney Monroe. He was an important abolitionist, advocate of voting rights for African-Americans, and friend of Frederick Douglass. The *Little Red Schoolhouse* (1836) was the first public school in town. It has been moved several times, most recently in 1968. Restored as a pioneer era one-room school, it is a special favorite of school age visitors who enjoy using the slate boards and McGuffey readers, trying out the dunce cap and stool in the corner. The brick Victorian-style *Jewett House* (1884) was the home of Oberlin College professor Frank Fanning Jewett, and his wife Frances Gulick Jewett, author of books on public health and hygiene. This is a wonderfully intact house with a simple wood frame barn on the property.
NRHP
Oberlin Historical and Improvement Organization
Photos courtesy of the Oberlin Historical and Improvement Organization

OKEANA

GOVERNOR WILLIAM BEBB BIRTHPLACE, 1799
Governor Bebb Preserve
7639 Cincinnati-Brookville Road
Okeana, Ohio 45053
Butler County
(513) 867-5835

May-September/Sun/1-5 or by appointment

This two-story hewn log house was built in 1799 and originally stood on a site along Dry Fork Creek near Okeana, about four miles from its present location. A unique feature of the house is a three-faced fireplace, which serves as a central heating source for the downstairs rooms. Purchased in 1801 by Edward Bebb, a Welsh

continued

immigrant, William Bebb was born here in 1802, reputedly the first white child born in Butler County. Raised here, he became a teacher and a lawyer, and was elected the nineteenth governor of Ohio, serving from 1846 to 1848. The house was occupied by various owners until 1959 when it was donated to the Butler County Park District. It was removed from its original site and reconstructed in what is now Governor William Bebb Preserve. Also located here is Pioneer Village, consisting of five log structures (c. 1800-1860); a school house, tavern, general store, meeting house and homestead.
Metro Parks of Butler County

OXFORD

McGUFFEY MUSEUM, 1833; additions
MIAMI UNIVERSITY ART MUSEUM
Spring and Oak Streets
Oxford, Ohio 45056
Butler County
(513) 529-2232

Sat-Sun/2-4
or by appointment
Closed August and University Holidays

William Holmes McGuffey, author and Miami University faculty member, built and lived in this two-story brick vernacular adaptation of a Federal style house for three years. After many owners, Miami University bought the house. The purpose of its restoration and refurbishing was to maintain its character as a private home that had been lived in over a long period of years. As a museum, it is a depository of the famous McGuffey readers, spellers, primers and thousands of children's textbooks published before 1900. Also there are McGuffey memorabilia and furnishings, documents, furniture, paintings and decorative pieces that have been donated.
NRHP-NHL
Miami University

PIONEER FARM AND HOUSE MUSEUM, 1830's-1840's
Brown Road, 3 miles north of Oxford
PO Box 184
Oxford, Ohio 45056
Butler County
(513) 523-6244 or (513) 523-5376

Memorial Day to mid-October/Sat-Sun/1-5
or by appointment

Donation

This simple Federal vernacular style brick house in its original setting was built and occupied by the Doty family. After multiple owners, the house was acquired by the State of Ohio and became part of Hueston Woods State Park. It has been restored and furnished as closely as possible to a three generation home of the mid-19th century.
NRHP
Oxford Museum Association

PIQUA

JOHN JOHNSTON FARM, 1808-1829
9845 North Hardin Road
Piqua Historical Area
Piqua, Ohio 45356
Miami County
(513) 773-2522

**Memorial Day-Labor Day/Wed-Sat/9:30-5
Sun/Noon-5
Labor Day-October 31/Sat/9:30-5
Sun/Noon-5**

Admission fee

The Johnston brick farmhouse was built in two parts; a Dutch Colonial style wing and a Georgian style wing. It is the only Indian Agency house in Ohio. During the War of 1812, Johnston was charged by the Federal Government with the supervision of the Indians who remained at peace with the United States. He had as many as 6,000 Indians at a time on his farm. Outbuildings include a log barn, fruit kiln, cider house and spring house. It is furnished with period furniture dating before 1830. A section of the Miami-Erie Canal runs past the property and authentic canal boat rides are available. Craft demonstrations such as cooking, candle dipping and spinning are periodically given throughout the season.
NRHP
Ohio Historical Society - OHS Photo

POINT PLEASANT

ULYSSES S. GRANT BIRTHPLACE 1817;

mid-century addition
U.S. 52 and S.R. 232
Point Pleasant, Ohio 45153
Clermont County
(513) 553-4911

**April 1-October 31/Wed-Sat/9:30-Noon, 1-5
Sun/Noon-5
or by appointment
Closed Mon, Tu, holidays**

Admission fee

Grant was born in this small one-room frame cottage in 1822. Items which belonged to the Grant family are on display. Ulysses S. Grant, one of eight Ohioans to become President of the United States, served from 1869 until 1877.
Ohio Historical Society

PORTSMOUTH

1810 HOUSE, 1810; 1812 additions
1926 Waller Street
One block from U.S. Route 23
turn on Kinneys Lane
Portsmouth, Ohio 45662
Scioto County
(614) 353-2099

**Mid-May to mid-December/Sat, Sun/2-4
or by appointment**

This Federal vernacular style brick house was built by Aaron and Mary Kinney, early Scioto County settlers, who raised twelve children here. Materials used in building came from the land on which it stands. The thick walls served as protection in the event of Indian attack. The classical portico was added in the early 20th century and turned the original farm house into a town house. The rooms are furnished in several 19th century periods and include some Kinney pieces, which reflect the life style of the three generations of Kinneys who lived here. Many articles of Americana are displayed and exhibits change periodically.
NRHP
Scioto County Historical Society

RAVENNA

CARTER HOUSE 1828; 1849; 1865
6549 North Chestnut Street
Ravenna, Ohio 44266
Portage County
(216) 296-3523

Tu-Th/Sun/2-4

The present Carter House was built in three stages; the original house, a section added in 1849 and the 1865 Greek Revival front. The interior reflects the time space of the house. Each room is furnished in a different period. The Carter family came to Ravenna Township from Connecticut in1806 and became prominent citizens. It is believed that at one time Erastus Carter Jr. ran a tavern in the house.
Portage County Historical Society

RIPLEY

RANKIN HOUSE STATE MEMORIAL, 1828
Rankin Road off U.S. 52
Ripley, Ohio 45167
Brown County
(513) 392-1627

Memorial Day-Labor Day
Wed-Sun, holidays/Noon-5
May, September, October/Sat, Sun/Noon-5
or by appointment

Admission fee

This simple vernacular style brick house was the home of the family of the Rev.John Rankin, a leading abolitionist and active "conductor" on the Underground Railroad from 1828 to 1863. At least twelve slaves could be hidden at the Rankin House at one time. Situated on Liberty Hill, it overlooks the Ohio River from which slaves climbed a steep stairway to the house and to freedom. It is restored and furnished with period pieces and personal Rankin items. The original steps, removed in 1986, have been replaced.
NRHP
Ohio Historical Society
Ripley Heritage, Inc.

SANDUSKY

ELEUTHEROS COOKE HOUSE, 1844
1415 Columbus Avenue
Sandusky, Ohio 44870
Erie County
(419) 627-0640

House restoration is on-going.
Call ahead for status and hours of operation.

This Greek Revival-style three story house was constructed for Eleutheros Cooke, Sandusky's first lawyer and father of Civil War financier and railroad promoter, Jay Cooke. The house was moved, piece by piece, from its original site at the corner of Columbus Avenue and Washington Row to its current location in 1878. Constructed of limestone, the house features a recessed paneled door flanked by fluted pilasters with a portico over the entry supported by two stone columns. Stone battlements surround the roof which supports four chimneys. The house contains a fine collection of antiques, cranberry glass, oriental rugs, and other items. It has original Greek Revival woodwork and several working fireplaces. It remains as it was restored in 1953.
NRHP
Old House Guild of Sandusky
Ohio Historical Society
Photo by Bill Schulz

FOLLETT HOUSE MUSEUM, 1834-1837
404 Wayne Street
Sandusky, Ohio 44870
Erie County
(419) 627-9608 or (419) 625-3834

June-Labor Day/Tu-Sun/1-4
Labor Day-December/April-May/Tu, Th, Sun/1-4

This handsome Greek Revival style stone house was built by Oran Follett. His multi-faceted career ranged from U.S. Navy, New York legislator, realtor, banker, editor and part-owner of the *Ohio State Journal* to railroad president. He fought against slavery and helped establish the Republican party. During the Civil War, Mr. Follett's wife Eliza removed furniture from the parlor to allow space for the Sanitary Commission, which enlisted women to make bandages, etc. Beginning in 1976, the Sandusky Library has used the house for its archival center and local history museum. Items in the collection reflect Erie County history from its earliest times to the present, including an outstanding collection of Civil War items from the confederate officers' prison on Johnson's Island.
NRHP
Sandusky Library Association

SHARONVILLE

SHARON WOODS VILLAGE, pre-1880
Located in Sharon Woods Park on U.S. 42
1 mile South of I-275, Sharonville Exit
Hamilton County
PO Box 62475
Cincinnati, Ohio 45262
(513) 563-9484

May-October/Wed-Fri/10-4
Sat and Sun/1-5
November and December special hours
guided tour available

Admission fee

Kemper Log House

This historical village is a return to the Ohio countryside of over 100 years ago. The Village includes nine historic southwestern Ohio buildings that were threatened with destruction at their original sites. Each building was moved to Sharon Woods Village, where it was authentically restored and furnished. The earliest building in the Village is the *Kemper Log House* (1804) also one of the earliest surviving homes in the Cincinnati area. Built by Rev. James Kemper, this two-story, squared-log house is owned by The National Society of the Colonial Dames of America in the State of Ohio. The *John Hayner House* (1840) is a spectacular example of a classical Greek Revival style farmhouse. The *Vorhes House* (1835) is a Federal style farmhouse where hearth-cooking demonstrations can be viewed.

continued

The small Steamboat Gothic *Langdon Medical Office* (1857) was built by Dr. Henry A. Langdon, a Union army member, and houses his examining room and medical office. *Chester Park Station* (1872) is a train station built in Cincinnati for the Baltimore and Ohio railroad. The *Elk Lick House* is an outstanding example of "Carpenter Gothic" architecture of the mid-19th century. The *Gatch Barn* was built in 1812. No nails were used framing the hand-hewn, pinned beams of this barn which contains a fine collection of 19th century farm implements. Buildings are completely furnished and visitors can view one of the finest collections of Ohio made furniture and decorative arts in the state. Other buildings in the Village include a general store (c. 1860) and early country church (c. 1829). The Village is located on 33 acres of land in Sharon Woods Park generously donated by the Hamilton County Park District.
Historic Southwest Ohio, Inc.

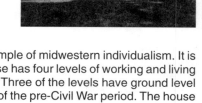

Elk Lick House

SPRINGFIELD

DANIEL HERTZLER HOUSE, 1854-1855
GEORGE ROGERS CLARK PARK
930 South Tecumseh
Route 4 west of
Springfield, Ohio 45506
Clark County
(513) 882-6000

April-October/second Sun of the month/1-4
or by appointment for groups

The Daniel Hertzler house is an interesting example of midwestern individualism. It is a bank style house with eight porches. The house has four levels of working and living space. Two of the levels are built into the bank. Three of the levels have ground level entries. The refurbished house has furnishings of the pre-Civil War period. The house overlooks the Revolutionary War Battle of Peckuwe area in the George Rogers Clark Park.
Clark County Park District.

PENNSYLVANIA HOUSE, mid-1820; additions

1311 West Main Street
Springfield, Ohio 45504
Clark County
(513) 322-7668 or (513) 322-8140

March-December
first Sun each month/1-4
except Christmas, New Year's Day
and Easter
or by appointment

Admission fee

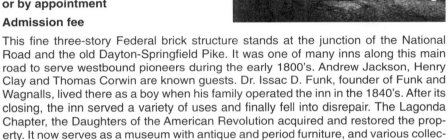

This fine three-story Federal brick structure stands at the junction of the National Road and the old Dayton-Springfield Pike. It was one of many inns along this main road to serve westbound pioneers during the early 1800's. Andrew Jackson, Henry Clay and Thomas Corwin are known guests. Dr. Issac D. Funk, founder of Funk and Wagnalls, lived there as a boy when his family operated the inn in the 1840's. After its closing, the inn served a variety of uses and finally fell into disrepair. The Lagonda Chapter, the Daughters of the American Revolution acquired and restored the property. It now serves as a museum with antique and period furniture, and various collections, which include dolls and buttons.

NRHP
Lagonda Chapter of the Daughters of the American Revolution
Photo by Charles A. Thomas

STOW

HERITAGE HOUSE MUSEUM, 1839

Young Road in Silver Spring Park
Stow, Ohio 44224
Summit County
(216) 650-0848 or (216) 688-1708

Early May-early December/1:30-4
or by appointment

Built at the intersection of the roads from Warren and Cleveland to Akron, this adaption of a Greek Revival style frame house became a stagecoach stop at what was known as Oregon Corners. Moved to its present location in 1972, it was restored and filled with many artifacts known to have been used in 1804 when settlers first came to the area. It has period furnishings. Of special interest is the open staircase with one spindle per step. The city of Stow has reserved the area where the Heritage House is located for the Historical Society's ongoing project of preservation. *Darrow House* (1850) has been moved to the area and restored and *Mary Starr House* (1850) is being restored and will be open to the public when complete.

Stow Historical Society

STRONGSVILLE

STRONGSVILLE HISTORICAL SOCIETY AND VILLAGE
13305 Pear Road
Strongsville, Ohio 44136
Cuyahoga County
(216) 243-3410 or (216) 238-1842

May-October/Wed, Sat, Sun/1-4
Tours by appointment

Admission fee

Chapman Cabin

The village was developed by Howard and Velda Chapman in 1957. They built the *Chapman Cabin* as a living example of the way life was in the early times from 1816 to about 1820. The authentic artifacts exemplify the way of life during that period. *Baldwin House* (1823) was one of the first wood frame houses in the center of Strongsville. This is an early Western Reserve Cottage that has been moved from its original site. Some alterations have been made to the basic house and the Society added the fireplace and period furnishings. *Roe-Chapman House* (1904) was built by a Mr. Pepper who built many homes in Strongsville. The gambrel roof (Dutch) is of interest. The interior of the house is filled with a variety of woods. This was the original property purchased by the Chapmans that was given to the Historical Society. There are other buildings on the property of interest.
Strongsville Historical Society

TOLEDO

MANOR HOUSE, 1938
Wildwood Preserve Metropark
1500 West Central Avenue
Toledo, Ohio 43615
Lucas County
(419) 535-3050

January-December/Wed-Sun/Noon-5
except Thanksgiving and the week following, Christmas and New Year's Day

The Manor House in Wildwood Preserve Metropark is not an historic house in the chronological sense; but in its ambience and craftsmanship it preserves a heritage of quality workmanship. The stately brick house was designed by the local firm of Bellman, Gillet and Richards in the 18th century Georgian Colonial style for a prominent Toledo businessman. It is set among acres of forest land and the front portico overlooks lawns and gardens. To the east is an Italian formal garden with brick walls, wrought iron gazebos and fountains. The interior exemplifies the Georgian style fine wood paneling, mantels and plaster work. Reproduction and period furniture is found in the twenty-two rooms open to the public. Special activities are offered and meetings can be arranged.
Metropolitan Park District of the Toledo Area

IDDINGS LOG HOUSE, c. 1804
Brukner Nature Center
5995 Horseshoe Bend Road
5 miles west of 1-75, exit 73
Troy, Ohio 45373
Miami County
(513) 698-6493

January-December/Mon-Sat/9-5/Sun/12:30-5

Admission fee on Sundays only

Located in the Brukner Nature Center, this two-story hewn log house is on its original site in Miami County. The house is minimally furnished and used extensively by schools for an early Ohio history program. It was built by Benjamin and Phoebe Iddings, prominent Quakers, for their family of ten children. Archeological studies have been conducted at the site and helped authenticate its restoration.
NRHP
Brukner Nature Center

OVERFIELD TAVERN MUSEUM, 1808
201 East Water Street
Troy, Ohio 45373
Miami County
(513) 335-4019

April-October/Th-Sat, Sun/2-4
or by appointment
Closed holidays

In 1807 when the site of Troy was chosen as the county seat of the newly formed Miami County, Benjamin Overfield, Jr., grandson of German pioneers and one of Troy's first citizens, erected a two-story hewn log tavern and a one-room log house in the rear to serve as private living quarters. The inn also served as a temporary meeting place for the courts for three years. Around the middle of the 19th century the Overfield Tavern and the homestead cabin were joined together, plastered on the interior and covered with siding on the exterior, but left on their original foundations. In 1948, the building was purchased and restored to its original appearance by Edward A. and William H. Hobart, Sr.. It contains early primitive furnishings that portray life on the frontier.
NRHP
Troy Historical Society

TROY-HAYNER CULTURAL CENTER, 1914

301 West Main Street
Troy, Ohio 45373
Miami County
(513) 339-0457

January-December/Tu-Sat/9-5
Mon-Th/7-9/Sun/1-5

This fine Norman-Romanesque style mansion was built by Mary Jane Harter Colman Hayner. It was designed by well-known architect Leonard B. Willeke. She lived in this spacious house with treasures she brought home from numerous trips abroad until her death in 1942. Mrs. Hayner left her home to the Troy Board of Education for educational purposes. The half-timbered eclectic house has a spectacular interior. The main rooms have decorative plaster moldings, coffered ceilings and classical marble mantlepieces. There are seven different patterns of leaded glass windows. The chandeliers are lead crystal. An attractive garden court is visible from the graceful stairway. Some furnishings and decorative pieces are original to the residence.
NRHP
Troy-Hayner Cultural Center

VAN WERT

GEORGE H. MARSH HOMESTEAD, 1861-1865; 1899

1229 East Ridge Road
Box 150
Van Wert, Ohio 45891
Van Wert County
(419) 238-1695 ext 120

by appointment only

This two-story cross-shaped brick house with a later Queen Anne addition was built by George H. Marsh. The interior has been restored to the Victorian period and contains Marsh family furniture and mementos. Marsh came to Van Wert at the age of twelve. After the Civil War, he began his career as a bookkeeper and later became a multi-millionaire. Funds from his will established the Marsh Foundation School for abandoned children. The school buildings (1925), on the site are fine examples of Jacobethan Revival style architecture.
NRHP
The Marsh Foundation

HOUSE OF SEVEN OAKS, 1898

Corner of North Washington and East Third streets
Van Wert, Ohio 45891
Van Wert County
(419) 238-3398 or (419) 238-5297

March-December/Sun/2-4:30
or by appointment

Donation

Mrs. John O. Clark drew plans for her family's Victorian home to be built of locally quarried blue limestone on land she had inherited. When their youngest child was born her husband planted an oak sapling from the virgin forest surrounding the town to join the six already on the property. There is a Victorian parlor furnished with period pieces, a music room with instruments typical of the era as well as a 19th century dining room and kitchen. Upstairs there is a fine example of an 1860 bedroom as well as a fabric room, reading room and toy room with 19th century appointments. On the grounds there is a 19th century school house.
Van Wert Historical Society

WARREN

JOHN STARK EDWARDS HOUSE, 1807

303 Monroe North West
Warren, Ohio 44483
Trumbull County
(216) 394-4653

Call for appointment

Admission fee

This early Western Reserve style frame house was built by John Stark Edwards. His father was a shareholder in the Connecticut Land Company and received as his portion all of Mesopotamia Township. John Edwards graduated from Yale Law School in 1799 and came to Mesopotamia to open up the area. In 1800 he was appointed Recorder of Trumbull County by Governor St. Clair of the Northwest Territory. The house has been restored and contains furnishings from the Edwards, Webb and Iddings families, and other appropriate furnishings and items of Americana.
NRHP
Trumbull County Historical Society
Photo by R.L. McCormack

HARRIET TAYLOR UPTON HOUSE, 1837

380 Mahoning Avenue N.W.
Warren, Ohio 44483
Trumbull County
(216) 399-1212 or (216) 395-1131

Tours by appointment

Donation

Warren was the capital of the Connecticut Western Reserve. Mahoning Avenue was once lined with lovely old homes. The Upton House is the third oldest home that survives. It was built in Greek Revival style by Henry B. Perkins, son of General Simon Perkins, surveyor and agent for the Connecticut Land Company. Judge Ezra Taylor bought the house in 1871. His daughter, Harriet, lived in the house until 1931. She was the national treasurer of the National American Woman's Suffrage Association and she moved the organization's headquarters to the library of her Mahoning Avenue home. The main floor is open to the public. It is furnished with Victorian pieces. Of special interest is the Egyptian Revival style architecture of the woodwork around the window and door openings. The restoration is on-going and is to include the beautiful gardens.
NRHP-NHL
Upton Associates, Inc.

WAYNESVILLE

CAESAR'S CREEK PIONEER VILLAGE, 1790-1848

Caesar's Creek State Park Area
Clarksville Road off S.R. 73
6 miles west of JCT I-71
Waynesville, Ohio 45068
Warren County
(513) 897-1120

Open year round
Buildings open by appointment Sat, Sun/8-9

Donation

The log home collection sits on the Levi Lukens Homestead c. 1807, with the original log home still intact on its foundation. The rest of the unique collection of log homes and one authentic log cabin were discovered during the construction of the Caesar's Creek Flood Control Project in 1970. These are original structures found and moved one piece at a time. There now are fifteen authentic log homes, two saddlebag cabins, one log cabin and a log barn. A rock spring house was recently reconstructed. Also there is an authentic Friends Meeting House (1848) which was moved to the village fully intact.
The Caesar's Creek Pioneer Village, Inc.
Caesar Creek State Park
Photo by L.R. Brock Creative Services

WESTERVILLE

HANBY HOUSE, 1846
160 West Main Street
Westerville, Ohio 43081
Franklin County
(614) 891-6289

**May-October/Sat/10-4/Sun, holidays/1-5
or by appointment**

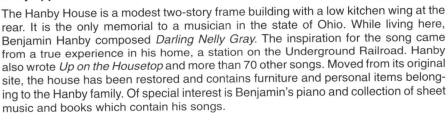

The Hanby House is a modest two-story frame building with a low kitchen wing at the rear. It is the only memorial to a musician in the state of Ohio. While living here, Benjamin Hanby composed *Darling Nelly Gray.* The inspiration for the song came from a true experience in his home, a station on the Underground Railroad. Hanby also wrote *Up on the Housetop* and more than 70 other songs. Moved from its original site, the house has been restored and contains furniture and personal items belonging to the Hanby family. Of special interest is Benjamin's piano and collection of sheet music and books which contain his songs.
NRHP
Ohio Historical Society
Westerville Historical Society

WEST LIBERTY

PIATT CASTLES, 1871, 1881
S.R. 245
West Liberty, Ohio 43357

CASTLE MAC-A-CHEEK
1 mile east West Liberty

CASTLE MAC-O-CHEE
2 miles east West Liberty
at junction of S.R. 245 and S.R. 287
Logan County
(513) 465-2821

Castle Mac-A-Cheek

**Both castles open March/Sat-Sun/Noon-4
April/daily/Noon-4/May-September/daily/Noon-4
Guided 45 minute tours
Group tours can be arranged by reservations**

Admission fee

In the midst of the historic Indian country of the Mac-A-Cheek Valley rise two castles; one Norman French (1864), and the other Flemish (1881), built by brothers renowned as military leaders and statesmen. They were sons of Benjamin Piatt who purchased this land in 1817. General Abram Saunders Piatt built his Norman *Castle Mac-A-Cheek*

continued

with its watchtower and two foot thick walls of hand chiseled limestone. The floors of walnut, oak and wild cherry, as well as the wall panelling were crafted from trees felled on the property. The furnishings are family pieces. *Castle Mac-O-Chee* was built by Colonel Donn Piatt who was President Pierce's charge d'affaires to the Count of Napoleon. He employed his nephew, William McCoy Piatt to design his Flemish castle of Ohio limestone. The painted walls and ceilings were executed by Oliver Frey of Mentone, France. Patterned in-laid oak and walnut floors compliment the collection of European, American, and Asiatic chairs, tables and art objects.
NRHP
Piatt Castles Co., Inc.

Castle Mac-O-Chee

WEST PORTSMOUTH

PHILIP MOORE JR. STONE HOUSE, c. 1797
Hill Road
West Portsmouth Ohio
c/o Dr. Louis and Ava Chaboudy
3330 Sheridan Road
Portsmouth, Ohio 45662
Scioto County
(614) 353-5605

by appointment only

This interesting old Pennsylvania stone house is an outstanding example of a primitive house of this period. It was built by Philip Moore, Jr., a Revolutionary War soldier who received 300 acres of Ohio land as mustering out pay. He went down the Ohio River on a flat boat to select his land. He and his wife Jemima, and four children lived in this house. It has a large room with a fireplace on each end on the entry floor. Up a narrow corner stairway there is a large sleeping room with a fireplace. Some of the original rough wood flooring is still visible on the main floor. The house is furnished with period pieces. The area was the cradle of Methodism and the circuit riders met in Moore's house to formulate policy.
NRHP
Dr. Louis and Ava Chaboudy

WILMINGTON

ROMBACH PLACE, 1831; additions
149 East Locust Street
Wilmington, Ohio 45177
Clinton County
(513) 382-4684

March-December/Wed-Fri/1-4:30

Genealogy library open by appointment

Used as a residence of the Denver family for four generations, the two-story brick structure with a gabled shingle roof was built in 1831 by Robert Wickersham. James W.
Denver, soldier, lawyer and statesman went to California for the gold rush in 1850. He
became involved in politics, first elected State Senator, then appointed Secretary of
State in 1853. In 1854 he was elected to Congress and appointed Commissioner of
Indian Affairs. In 1856 he returned to Wilmington and married Louise Rombach, daughter of a prominent banker. Rombach Place became their home and remained in the
family for 99 years. Among items on display are antique furniture, Quaker clothing, bronze
animal sculptures, paintings by Eli Harvey and photographic portraits of Indian Chieftains by Karl Moon. A genealogy library is available. A Victorian barn has artifacts.
NRHP
Clinton County Historical Society

WOOSTER

GENERAL REASIN BEALL HOME, 1815
546 East Bowman Street
Wooster, Ohio 44691
Wayne County
(216) 264-8856

January-December/Tu-Sun/2-4:30
Special group tours by appointment
closed holidays

Admission fee

This simple Georgian style brick home was built by General Reasin Beall, who served
in the Continental Army and was a land grant commissioner and Congressman. In its
day the house was the oldest and finest in town with a central hallway extending from
front to rear on each floor and an open staircase. Many of the 19th century furnishings
are original to the house. A variety of exhibits include lighting devices, fashions, tools,
household utensils, portraits and military weapons. Outside, there is a log house of
the Civil War period containing pioneer furniture and a one-room school house (c.
1873). A reference library, genealogical service and meeting space are available.
NRHP
Wayne County Historical Society
Photo courtesy of Wayne County Historical Society

THE OLD RECTORY, 1845; additions
50 West New England Avenue
Worthington, Ohio 43085
Franklin County
(614) 885-1247

**Jan-December 15/Tu-Fri/1-5
or by appointment
Special tours should be arranged six weeks in advance**

Admission fee

The Old Rectory was built as the rectory for St. John's Episcopal Church in Worthington, the first Episcopal Church west of the Alleghenies. This Greek Revival manse was acquired by the Worthington Historical Society in 1978 and is now elegantly restored. The Old Rectory features a magnificent needlepoint rug stitched by members of the Society and the local Chapter of the Embroiderers' Guild of America. It also houses a beautifully displayed doll museum, one of the most extensive doll collections in the area. Special exhibits, a library with many historical publications, an expanding re-source center and the Society offices also call the Old Rectory their home.

ORANGE JOHNSON HOUSE 1811; addition 1830
956 High Street
Worthington, Ohio 43085
Franklin County
(614) 885-1247

**January-December 15/Sun/2-5
or by appointment 6 weeks ahead
Closed Thanksgiving weekend
Christmas and Easter**

Admission fee

The Orange Johnson House was built by Arora Buttles. In 1816 Orange Johnson, a hornsmith and combmaker, and his wife, Achsa Maynard Johnson, purchased the house for $1,500. By 1819, Johnson's financial success enabled him to add a Federal house to the front of the original residence. The Worthington Historical Society pur-chased this property in 1962. After extensive restoration, the House was opened in 1972. The residence stands as the only pioneer home in Franklin County on its origi-nal foundation that is open to the public. The House features authentic furnishings of the period, some from Worthington.
NRHP
Worthington Historical Society

XENIA

GREENE COUNTY HISTORICAL SOCIETY HOUSE, 1877; additions
74 West Church Street
Xenia, Ohio 45385
Greene County
(513) 372-4606

**January-December/Tu-Fri/9-Noon/1-3:30
Tours 1:30
May-October/Tu-Fri/9-noon-1-3:30
Tours 1:30/Sat-Sun/1-4
or by appointment**

Admission fee

This Queen Ann Victorian home was built in 1877, and was enlarged to its present size shortly thereafter. In 1977, it was moved next to *James Galloway Log House* (c. 1798). The furnishings in the home are appropriate to the era. In addition, there is a collection of oil paintings some of which picture early residents of the county. James Galloway, first Treasurer of Greene County, built his log house for his wife and five children. Originally near the bend of the Little Miami River, north of Old Chillicothe, the house has since been moved twice. Galloway was an influential man in the community, visited by Shawnee Chieftains Tecumseh and Blue Jacket, and by George Rogers Clark and Simon Kenton. There is also a Carriage House Museum.
Greene County Historical Society

YOUNGSTOWN

GREYSTONES, 1905
648 Wick Avenue
Youngstown, Ohio 44502
Mahoning County
(216) 743-2589

**January-December/Tu-Fri/1-4
or by appointment
Group Tours/9-4
closed holidays
All tours are guided**

Admission fee

An outstanding example of the Arts and Crafts style, the house was designed by the architectural firm of Meade and Garfield with the assistance of Olive Freeman Arms. The stone exterior and roof lines are reminiscent of English country homes. Some details relate to the late medieval and early Renaissance period by the use of leaded glass and wrought iron. Pioneer artifacts, antique toys and Indian War relics are displayed. It is located in the Wick Avenue Historic District.
Arms Museum of The Mahoning Valley Historical Society

ZANESVILLE

DR. INCREASE MATHEWS HOUSE, 1805; 1834
304 Woodlawn Avenue
Zanesville, (Putnam), Ohio 43701
Muskingum County
(614) 454-9500

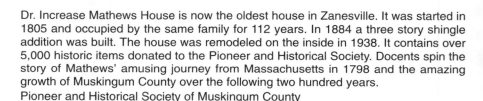

May-October/Tu-Fri/10-3/Sun/2-4:30

Admission fee

Dr. Increase Mathews House is now the oldest house in Zanesville. It was started in 1805 and occupied by the same family for 112 years. In 1884 a three story shingle addition was built. The house was remodeled on the inside in 1938. It contains over 5,000 historic items donated to the Pioneer and Historical Society. Docents spin the story of Mathews' amusing journey from Massachusetts in 1798 and the amazing growth of Muskingum County over the following two hundred years.
Pioneer and Historical Society of Muskingum County

THE STONE ACADEMY, 1809
113 Jefferson Street
Zanesville, Ohio 43701
Muskingum County
(614) 454-9500

May-October/Tu-Fri/10-3/Sun/2-4:30

Admission fee

The Stone Academy was built by the founders of (Putnam) Zanesville with the hopes it would become the next state capital building of Ohio. In the 1830's the State Aboli-tion Society held riotous meetings here. In 1872 it was the home of Elizabeth Robbins, who grew up to become an actress. She toured the United States with James Booth and introduced Hedda Gabler to the London stage. The eclectic furnishings of the house are representative of its history. Also there are local history displays, including textiles and paintings which are changed yearly.
Pioneer and Historical Society of Muskingum County

ZOAR

ZOAR VILLAGE STATE MEMORIAL, 1817-1898
Main Street (S.R. 212)
Zoar, Ohio 44697
Tuscarawas County
(216) 874-3011

Memorial Day-Labor Day/Wed-Sat/9:30-5
Sun, Mon, holidays/Noon-5
April-Memorial Day,
September-October/Sat, Sun/Noon-5
Appointments for groups

Admission fee

Number One House

Zoar Village was founded in 1817 by Joseph Baumeler and a group of Separatists from Germany and it became a Christian communal society. Originally, *Number One House* (1835), a Georgian brick and stone house with a two-story portico housed the community's aged and infirm. Later it became the home of Baumeler and two other families. The center stairway extends to the attic, where on the ceiling of the stairwell is the colored seven pointed star, the Zoar emblem. Other German vernacular buildings on the site include the bakery (1845), greenhouse (1835), store (1833), kitchen (1835), magazine storehouse (1845), dairy (1841), and reproductions of the tin, wagon and blacksmith shops.
NRHP
Ohio Historical Society

HISTORIC BUILDINGS WITH DINING FACILITIES

A few historic inns and taverns are included in this guide for the convenience of our readers. It is only a sampling of the many historic dining facilities in Ohio. Commercial establishments are not the focus of this publication.

THE HERITAGE, 1827
7664 Wooster Pike
Cincinnati, Ohio 45227
Hamilton County

Open year round-regular dining hours
(513) 561-9300

This federal style brick house was built by Edgar and Martha Scott 12 miles east of Cincinnati. The Wooster Turnpike passed in front of the house. It was a busy road alive with stagecoaches and covered wagons. By the turn of the century the Scott home became the area's most fashionable restaurant. It's present owners have re-stored it beautifully and retained the huge wooden beams above the bar and tack room. There is an extensive collection of Indian artifacts throughout the building.
Howard and Jan Melvin

THE GRAND FINALE, 1875
Sharon Road at Congress Avenue
Glendale, Ohio 45246
Hamilton County

Open year round-regular dining hours
Closed Mondays
(513) 771-5925

This lovely restaurant is in a Victorian Style house that is one of the most historic buildings in Glendale. It had a varied history until 1975 when the present owners purchased the building and began its restoration. The tin ceiling is original. The back bar and grand chandelier are from other historic spots as are many of the lovely antique furnishings and artifacts.
Larry and Cindy Youse

BUXTON INN, 1812
313 East Broadway
Granville, Ohio 43023
Licking County

Open year round-regular dining hours
(614) 587-0001

The lovely old Buxton Inn was built in 1812 when Orrin Granger, a pioneer from Granville, Massachusetts built it as *The Tavern*. Known as the Buxton since 1865 it has been operated continuously and is one of the oldest Inn's in Ohio. Mr. and Mrs. Orville Orr purchased it in 1972 and began extensive research and restoration. The Buxton offers food and lodging in a welcoming Victorian atmosphere.
NRHP
Orville and Audrey Orr

HISTORIC BUILDINGS WITH DINING FACILITIES

THE RED BRICK TAVERN, 1837   **Open year round-regular dining hours**
U.S. Route 40 at Lafayette   **(513) 652-1474 or 1-800-343-6118**
Halfway between Columbus & Springfield
Madison County

This famous landmark is Ohio's second oldest inn that remains in operation. Its design is English Manor style. Still visible are the broad double chimneys on either side of the roof and the deep set windows with rippling glass panes, original wood trim and the original fireplaces. Today the fragrance of baking hams and other American specialites greet guests.
NRHP
Privately owned

GOLDEN LAMB INN, 1815; additions   **Open year round-regular dining hours,**
27 South Broadway   **reservations suggested**
Lebanon, Ohio 45036   **(513) 932-5065 or 621-8373**
Warren County

In 1803 Jonas Seaman was issued a license to operate "a house of public entertainment". In 1815 a two-story Federal style brick building replaced the original log tavern. The Golden Lamb is also a Shaker museum and houses an extensive collection of Shaker furniture and artifacts. Visitors are encouraged to explore the upper floors and view the Inn's antique collections and Currier and Ives prints.
NRHP
Privately owned

MALABAR INN, 1820   **Open mid-March to October**
3645 Pleasant Valley Road   **regular dining hours, closed Mondays**
Perrysville, Ohio 44864   **(419) 938-5205**
Richland County

The Malabar Inn was built by David Shrack and his sons along one of the busiest routes of the day. The enormous spring which flows from the hillside behind the Inn was a welcome stop for travelers to and from markets along Lake Erie and the Ohio River. In 1941 the brick house and surrounding property became part of Malabar Farm. The Malabar Inn was opened as a country inn in 1963.
Malabar Farms State Park

HISTORIC BUILDINGS WITH DINING FACILITIES

THE FEDERAL HOUSE, 1830
429 Second Street
PO Box 314
Portsmouth, Ohio 45662
Scioto County

Open year round-regular dining hours
Closed Sunday and Monday
(614) 353-5116

The Federal House was built by William Hall and was his residence until his death in 1869. The house had a varied history until it was purchased and restored by its present owners to be used as a restaurant. The metal fireplaces and the wide woodwork might be original. The tiger maple circular stairway was installed as part of an 1850 remodeling.

Pete and Diane Warren

OLIVER HOUSE, 1859
27 Broadway Street
Toledo, Ohio 43602
Lucas County

Open year round-regular dining hours
closed Thanksgiving & Christmas
Reservations suggested
(419) 234-1302

Commissioned by Major William Oliver (War of 1812), this beautiful hotel was designed in the Greek Revival style by nationally prominent architect Isaiah Rogers. Two ornamental mantles and a black walnut and ash floor in the lobby area remain. Today Oliver House has been renovated to reflect its architectural and historical significance.

NRHP
Privately owned

THE OLD TAVERN, 1708; additions
Route 84 at County Line Road
Exit 218 off I-90 at Geneva
Unionville, Ohio 44088
Ashtabula County

Open year round-regular dining hours
closed Monday
(216) 428-2091 or 1-800-7-TAVERN
(782-8376)

The original Old Tavern was one of the first log cabins built on the Western Reserve. It has an interesting history as a stopping place for covered wagons from Pittsburgh, "the gateway to the West". Wooden pillars were added to the two story salt box in honor of General Lafayette in 1926. During the abolition movement it became a station for the Underground Railroad and maintains much atmosphere of the old days today.

NRHP
Privately Owned

HISTORIC BUILDINGS WITH DINING FACILITIES

COLUMBIAN HOUSE, 1828
3 North River Road
Waterville, Ohio 43566
Lucas County

Open year round-regular dining hours
closed Monday and Tuesday
(419) 878-3006

This wonderful frontier inn is considered one of the purest examples of Federal style, with Greek revival influences, in Northwest Ohio. It was build by John Pray, town founder. Constructed of native oak, ash, walnut and poplar, the building has refined moldings, fireplaces on all floors, period furnishings and a dramatic third floor. It offers unique atmosphere and fine food as it has for 50 years.
NRHP
Privately owned

WELSHFIELD INN c. 1840's
14001 Main Market Road
U.S. Route 422
Welshfield, Ohio 44021
Geauga County

Open year round-regular dining hours
closed Monday
(216) 834-4164 or 1-800-882-1144

The Inn was built by Alden Nash and was known in subsequent years as the Nash Hotel. It was a stagecoach stop between Youngstown and Cleveland. During the Civil War, the Inn was an Underground Railroad stop. The present owners offer an attractive menu.

Stefee Family

THE WORTHINGTON INN, 1834; additions and enlargements
649 High Street
Worthington, Ohio 43085
Franklin County

Open year round-regular dining hours
(614) 885-2600

Mr. R.W. Cowles came to Worthington from Connecticut. He married Laura Kilbourne and built his residence which later became known as The Worthington Inn. By 1983 The Inn had changed hands many times and was in a state of disrepair. Through careful planning and research it has been transformed into one of the most distinguished Victorian Inns in Ohio.
Privately owned

* Indicates Inn or Tavern with dining facilities

INDEX BY COUNTY   PAGE

INDEX BY MUNICIPALITY   PAGE

*Indicates Inn or Tavern with dining facilities

107

INDEX BY MUNICIPALITY   PAGE

INDEX BY MUNICIPALITY   PAGE

INDEX BY MUNICIPALITY

ORDER FORM

A GUIDE TO HISTORIC HOUSES IN OHIO — OPEN TO THE PUBLIC
Betts House Research Center, Inc.
416 Clark Street
Cincinnati, Ohio 45203
(513) 651-0734
FAX: (513) 651-2143

Please send _____ copies of **A GUIDE TO HISTORIC HOUSES IN OHIO**
@ $10.50 plus $2.50 for postage and handling per copy.

Enclosed is $ _____

Ohio residents add 6.5% sales tax to the total order.

Checks may be made out to NSDASO and sent to the above address.

All copies will be sent to the same address unless otherwise specified.

Send to:

_____
NAME

_____
ADDRESS

_____
CITY   STATE   ZIP CODE